Charles Darwin

Charles Darwin

PIONEER IN THE THEORY OF EVOLUTION

H. E. L. MELLERSH

FREDERICK A. PRAEGER, *Publishers*
New York • Washington

BOOKS THAT MATTER

Published in the United States of America in 1969
by Frederick A. Praeger, Inc., Publishers
111 Fourth Avenue, New York, N.Y. 10003

© 1964 by H. E. L. Mellersh

Library of Congress Catalog Card Number: 68-55015

Printed in the United States of America

Contents

List of Illustrations

Charles Darwin

I

Geologists, Biologists, and the Old Testament

CHARLES DARWIN, aged twenty-three, gazed from the deck of H.M.S. *Beagle* upon the bleak shores of Tierra del Fuego, as yet uncharted and unexplored, and with a thrill of humble pride vowed that he "could employ his life no better than in adding a little to Natural Science." How big that "little" became the world now knows.

But at that date, 1832, the young Charles still regarded himself as an amateur and expected to settle down after the voyage as a quiet and inoffensive country clergyman. That one day his writings were to make history and to shock even a bishop into impassioned abuse was as unsuspected by him as was the fact that the monkeys along the coast of South America, or anywhere else, would be recognized as the distant relatives of mankind.

That Charles should have ever sailed upon that all-important voyage was the result, as we shall see, of such a prolonged series of accidents and coincidences as to make one think that Fate, already aware of what lay in the balance, had decided that he must go. To say that in 1832 nobody had ever heard of the idea of organic evolution* would be untrue, but, in 1832, nobody could prove it as a fact or even as a reasonable proposition, few people believed in it, and most of those who knew of it reacted violently against it.

Before we tell of Charles Darwin's life and of the events that led up to the famous voyage, we must take a look at what was happening in the scientific world, and in the world of natural science in particular. We must take a brief glance at those first decades of the nineteenth century, when the Industrial Revolution was really getting into its stride and when, in the country that was leading that revolution, the later Hanoverian kings were, in their not entirely admirable ways, setting the scene that would blossom forth into the prosperity and ferment of the Victorian Era.

What is difficult for us to realize is—not to put too fine a point on it—the ignorance of the world of our great-, great-, great-grandfathers, i.e., of five generations ago, which, if we take an average generation as thirty years, brings us back to the second decade of the nineteenth century. Lest we be too proud, let us first realize that the educated person knew a good deal that many people now would not bother to know, such as the texts of the Bible and the classics, classical history, and contemporary poetry—one of the young midship-

---

* The meaning of this and other such terms will, it is hoped, become clear as we go along; but there is a Glossary at the end of the book that may help further.

men on H.M.S. *Beagle* could boast that "he had read all Byron and didn't care a damn for anybody!" But an immensity of scientific facts that we take absolutely for granted had not then been discovered—and nobody can know what has not been discovered.

Ignorance, however, is not a blank, and people usually have preconceived ideas about things of which they know little, ideas with which they are very loath to part: The untutored savage is not going to accept your assertion that the earth is round when he firmly believes that he can see with his own eyes that it is flat. The men and women of the early nineteenth century were hardly savages, but they were untutored in so far as knowledge was not yet there to be acquired.

One of the sciences where ignorance had been profound, but where the tutoring was already going on apace, was *geology*. Except for some pertinent questionings by the early Greeks and by that superinquirer Leonardo da Vinci, nobody had worried much about the earth's crust and its formation until the eighteenth century. Then it became apparent that the earth's crust was very old; that it was laid down, like a jam sandwich or a Neapolitan ice, in layers, or strata, which, however, were often very jumbled, bent, and contorted; and that these layers often contained the fossilized remains of once living creatures.

All this was disturbing. For the new knowledge challenged not only previously held beliefs but also the kind of belief that is most emotionally and tenaciously held, the religious kind. In the early seventeenth century, an Irish bishop, James Ussher, had dated the Bible back to Adam and Eve and the creation of the world—the latter, he asserted, had occurred in the year 4004 B.C. These dates had become incorporated in the margins of most Bibles and were as sacred and unalterable as the text itself. Nobody was prepared, therefore, to contemplate the enormous span of years for which, it now appeared, the world had existed. There was also the biblical account of the divine creation of the world, where "the waters covered the earth" before any rocks appeared, but where green things grew before even the sun was created.

Some of the early geologists managed to interpret all their findings in terms of the old beliefs; some of them compromised. There was Hugh Miller, an ex-stonemason, who told how the quarrymen, working in the Old Red Sandstone, christened the fossils of outstretched giant sea scorpions that they found as "seraphim" or winged angels. Miller recognized that there had existed many quite different and more primitive forms of life in the past, but he held that the "Prime Cause" had then, as it were, merely been "working greatly under its strength" and that the new zoological evidence was wholly *in favor* of revealed religion. There were others—and Darwin suffered under the lecturings of one of these—who, remembering their Old Testament, asserted that all rocks, including the volcanic ones, must have been formed originally from water. These were the "Neptunists," who quarreled interminably with the "Vulcanists," who held the view that subterranean heat had been primarily responsible. Then there was the important and fiercely held "Catastrophe" theory, which claimed that there had been, at periods throughout the world's history, catastrophic or cataclysmic events—times of terrible flood and fire, Noah's flood being one such occasion—when many, or most, or all, forms of animal life had been destroyed. After each catastrophe, God had simply started creating all over again.

Better things were to come, however. Two Scotsmen, James Hutton and Sir Charles Lyell, one after the other, had the strength of mind and the clarity of vision to declare roundly that the earth was immensely ancient and that the processes that had formed it were not strange and imagined "catastrophes" but constant and continuous and natural changes that were, in fact, still *in action.* Charles Darwin, as we shall see, was to owe much to Charles Lyell, who was his senior by only a dozen years.

The science of biology was also in its infancy and was very much bound by beliefs in a literal interpretation of the Old Testament. Much had been done to describe and systematize plant and animal life and to divide it into species, orders, and families of similarity. But that did not prevent all but a very few from believing implicitly in the separate creation of all living forms. Like the flat-earth enthusiasts of a past age, they had only to believe their eyes and their common sense: There existed Man, there existed Animals, and there existed Plants; God in His wisdom had created them like that, and that some of each kind might bear close and remarkable similarities to each other was of no particular significance and, in fact, was probably only to be expected.

Yet, even before Charles Darwin, there were men who were questioning the old biological assumptions, and who were doing so with surprising insight and pertinacity. One was the Frenchman with the resounding title of Jean Baptiste Pierre Antoine de Monet, Chevalier de Lamarck, commonly known as Lamarck. Another was Erasmus Darwin, Charles Darwin's grandfather.

Both Lamarck and Erasmus Darwin espoused the idea that the forms of life were not a series but a *connected* series that changed and grew over a long series of births and new generations. Lamarck went further and suggested a method by which this process of evolution had come about. It is a suggestion that some people today still believe to be fruitful but that most believe untenable; in any case, it was a suggestion that Lamarck could not and, indeed, did not even try to substantiate by proof.

It is, of course, one thing to bring forth suggestions and another to produce proof. And it is the second that Charles Darwin succeeded in doing, and with a thoroughness that is one apsect of his greatness. We shall be coming across the Chevalier de Lamarck again before we have finished. And, as for Erasmus Darwin, because he was Charles's grandfather and because, like the rest of us, Charles owed much to heredity and, at the same time, came from an outstanding family, we shall be considering this portly eighteenth-century gentleman in the chapter that follows.

2

Grandfather,
Father, Son

CHARLES'S GRANDFATHER Erasmus Darwin had his own pet definition of a fool—"a man who never tried an experiment in his life." As Dr. Erasmus naturally did not consider himself a fool, the definition tells us quite a bit about the speaker. He was a man of vivid imagination, always bubbling with new notions, throwing forth ideas as lesser men will crack jokes or utter pointless platitudes. He once invented, made, and installed a speaking tube and nearly scared a servant out of her wits at the sound of his disembodied voice. He fitted out his carriage with aids for reading and other gadgets so that he need not waste his time. He was a founder-member of the Lunar Club at Birmingham, the members of which (sometimes called "the Lunatics") met to dine and discuss science and art and "anything new" and

timed their meetings to the full moon so that the journey
home should be easier. He became an ardent amateur botanist
and breeder of livestock, as well as an author and poet.

In fact, he became a famous man. And his published
poetry—some of which reached what we should call the best-
seller level—took as its subjects, in a way that in those days
did not seem so curious, the occupations of his business and
his spare time: doctoring, physiology, pathology, botany,
and zoology. He gave his poems such titles as *The Loves of
the Plants*, *The Temple of Nature*, and *Zoonomia*, which
may be translated as "The Ways of Life." Whereas the modern botanist would tell us boldly that the mimosa is sensitive
to touch and responsive to light, or heliotropic, Erasmus
Darwin wrote:

> Weak with nice sense, the chaste Mimosa stands,
> From each rude touch withdraws her timid hands;
> .   .   .   .   .   .
> Shuts her sweet eyelids to approaching night;
> And hails with freshen'd charms the rising light.

Letting his fancy roam, he predicted in *Zoonomia:*

> Soon shall thy arm, Unconquer'd steam! afar
> Drag the slow barge, or drive the rapid car;
> Or on wide-waving wings expanded bear
> The flying chariot through the fields of air.
> —Fair crews triumphant, leaning from above,
> Shall wave their fluttering kerchiefs as they move;
> Or warrior bands alarm the gaping crowd,
> And armies shrink beneath the shadowy cloud.

It is a pity that the prophecy about warrior bands has proved more accurate than that of the fluttering kerchiefs.

There were, however, long and serious footnotes in prose, and these we should perhaps find most rewarding today. It was mostly in footnotes in *Zoonomia* that Erasmus Darwin expounded his startling views on the animal species, which, he held, were not unchanging and immutable but contained within themselves the power, through the generations, to develop. This almost amounted to stealing Charles's thunder before he was capable of making any himself, being as yet unborn. No one at the time, however, took very much notice of this part of *Zoonomia*, and what Charles thought of it, when he dutifully read his grandfather's book, we shall see anon. Erasmus, in fact, though one might on the face of it assume otherwise, was more important to his famous grandson as a purveyor of hereditary characteristics than as an author writing on the same subject matter.

Charles's father, Robert Darwin, was almost as forceful a character as was Erasmus. He was even bigger physically, a great mountain of a man. He followed in his father's profession of medicine, but moved his practice and became the foremost doctor in the town of Shrewsbury.

Robert also was a fount of ideas, but a great talker rather than a great writer. He had, said his son Charles of him later, an enormous interest in people, as well as a great sensitivity and a great kindness. He was loved as a doctor, therefore, and became to many of his patients something like a father-confessor. But he himself loved nothing so much as talking; he basked in his local fame and, to his family at least, could be more than a little overwhelming. They spoke of his return to the house in the evening as "the tide coming in."

Charles came fifth in a family of six, being born at Shrewsbury on February 12, 1809, with three sisters and a brother before him. His mother was a Wedgwood, member of the family of potters as famous in their way as the Darwins and a family that was to have a very considerable influence on Charles's life. Mrs. Darwin died, however, when Charles was only eight years old, and he confesses to remembering little about her. From then on, he was brought up by his elder sisters—Caroline, in particular—with "the tide" always in the offing.

We know quite a bit about Charles Darwin's boyhood and youth, because as an old man he wrote about it for the benefit of his children and grandchildren. He seems to have led a rather repressed and not altogether happy childhood, though exactly what effect that had on him is not easy to tell and may be left to the psychologists to analyze. He admits of Caroline that, on entering a room where she was, he would ask himself, "What will she blame me for now?" and that she was "too zealous in trying to improve me." His father, however, was wise enough to make light of his propensity for telling startling fibs in order to draw attention to himself.

Charles seems to have had a pleasantly simple and gullible nature. One day, a young friend took him into a sweetshop where he was known and could "get tick" and then into another, similar one. This apparent free purchase of desirables was achieved, he explained, by his wearing his father's hat and by tweaking it in a certain way as a sign when he was served. Would Charles like to try? Charles would. When he was jumped on by the irate shopkeeper as, after the approved tweak, he went to leave the shop with his free cakes, Charles was deeply hurt. He was not above telling his companion, however, that he had the wonderful power of making flowers change color by watering them with various tinted liquids.

In due course, Charles went to the famous Shrewsbury School, which was then climbing out of a period of neglect and was headed by a stern disciplinarian, who with a sort of fierce stubbornness saw to it that his boys were taught virtually nothing but the classics. Darwin asserts roundly that he learned nothing there; the school as a means of education to him "was simply a blank."

How many famous men, one wonders, have professed to doing poorly at school and to have gotten little or nothing from their schooling. Hardly enough, perhaps, to make bad schooling a good idea; as a start, one no doubt has to possess an embryonic greatness in order to be able to benefit from the situation. Charles must have had that germ. For one thing, he became a collector.

There may be nothing wonderful nor very unusual in that, perhaps. But, what is more unusual, he never lost the habit, although his collecting became somewhat more specialized. As a boy, his taste was catholic: shells and the names of flowers, seals and signatures, coins and minerals, insects and bird's eggs—of the latter, only once did he take the whole nestful "from a sort of bravado." Charles also became a lonely, self-sufficient, and thoughtful young person—sitting alone and reading to himself either *The Wonders of the World* or Shakespeare (not the comedies or the tragedies but the historical plays); fishing through long hours; going for long walks, where he became so absorbed by his thoughts that he once fell off a seven-foot parapet. A dog would accompany his walks, for he had developed a passion for dogs.

Then, as he approached his seventeenth birthday, full of self-taught knowledge, a slight admiration for the logical neatness of Euclid and the wit of Horace, but otherwise willfully ignorant of any school learning whatever, Charles Darwin left school and started preparing for his vocation.

And what was that vocation to be? The answer was, naturally, the profession that his father and grandfather had so graced—or, rather, considering their size, perhaps a better word would be, covered. So, young Darwin, himself tall, though certainly not corpulent, began, at this early age, his training to become a doctor. He joined his elder brother, another Erasmus, at Edinburgh.

There, the same pattern continued. Charles hated a good deal of what he was taught, or else he despised the teachers; but he learned what he wanted to learn. He found the then current geological disputes tedious. Anatomy and the practice of dissection not only bored but nauseated him—later, he was to bewail this lack of knowledge. He preferred going for long botanizing or entomologizing walks with like-minded friends or prowling around the rock pools of the estuary with Dr. Robert E. Grant, with whom he had struck up an acquaintance. Chemistry, too, he found very interesting, as did his brother, and he also felt that the art of taxidermy was worth learning. But, for the rest, the holidays were the best part of life.

Charles had graduated in his holidays, from a love of dogs to a love of the sporting life, out shooting with the dogs. In particular, he found this pleasant on the estate of

Maer, twenty miles away, the home of his Wedgwood cousins and his admired Uncle Jos. And, after all, since he believed that his father would leave him property enough to live on with comfort, why worry too much about those boring lectures in the next term ahead?

His stern father, however, was worrying, even if Charles was not. Already, he had accused his son of caring "for nothing but shooting, dogs and rat-catching" and warned him that he would be a disgrace to himself and to his family. After two years at Edinburgh, Charles was interviewed, and agreed apologetically that he did not want to be a doctor. There were in Robert Darwin's estimation very few feasible alternatives. His son had better transfer from Edinburgh to Cambridge and become a clergyman. Charles meekly agreed and industriously started polishing up his Greek for the entrance exam.

Charles must have had a lovely time at Cambridge. It would not be true to say that he did not work—he took his B.A. (mathematics, classics, and some moral philosophy in a nonhonors degree) as high as tenth on the list. He got in with a sporting and hunting set, "with jolly singing and playing of cards afterwards," and a musical set, with opportunity to hear, with a shiver down his back, the anthem in King's College Chapel. He even hired the choristers to sing in his rooms.

Charles also attended the lectures and the "delightful" expeditions of the botany professor John S. Henslow, a choice that was to have far-reaching consequences. In fact, with his usual youthful perversity, Darwin was sitting at the feet of Henslow and his colleagues with much greater assiduity than he was at the feet of those whose lectures he ought to have attended. His beetle hunting soon became an enthusiasm—for fear of losing others, he once popped one in his mouth and it tasted horrid—and Henslow soon grew to be more of a companion than a teacher, so that Charles became known at Cambridge as "the man who walks with Henslow." There was deep admiration here, and not only for Henslow's wide knowledge but for his striking character.

Darwin tells a story that is illustrative of the times through which they were living, as well as of Henslow's character. It was the age when medical students could obtain corpses for their knowledge of anatomy only by enlisting the help of "body snatchers," and these men were naturally highly unpopular. Once, in the Cambridge streets, the two men encountered a horrible procession wherein an angry crowd was dragging along two body snatchers that it had seized from the police and was very near lynching. Henslow took the lead in the effort to release them; on finding himself frustrated, he rushed to the mayor and at least saw to it that the miserable offenders reached prison alive.

In his last year at Cambridge, Charles was persuaded by Henslow to try to forget that early distaste for geology that the dull Edinburgh lectures had given him; before long, he found the subject fascinating, and tackled it with his usual enthusiasm. He must have shown an aptitude, as well as enthusiasm, for the last summer holiday after he left Cambridge found Charles striding across the Welsh hills on a geologizing expedition with, as companion, a professor of geology of some considerable fame, Adam Sedgwick. There would be the usual season's shooting at Maer to follow; but, after that, Charles would have to settle down to taking holy orders and to starting his career in the Church.

Charles, still very much the sporting man in spite of his new interests and enthusiasms, actually left Sedgwick still geologizing in Wales to go home early so that he might not miss a day of the shooting. And, in fact, he was very glad that he had done so; for waiting for him at home was a letter from Henslow, which nobody apparently had thought it worthwhile to send on to him.

3

The Chance of
a Lifetime

THERE WAS a certain Captain FitzRoy, of the Royal Navy, aristocrat and autocrat, who, although only twenty-six years of age, had already behind him the beginnings of a distinguished career. Having been on a surveying expedition to the coasts of South America and having taken over command during the expedition, the young captain was now about to return to those parts and to continue on a longer surveying voyage around the world.

Now, Robert FitzRoy had an inquiring mind and, at that time at least, a confident disposition. He had conceived the idea that it would be well to have a naturalist on board during this second voyage, an expert with knowledge of geology and zoology, and he persuaded the Admiralty that his idea was a good one. There would be no pay attached to the post, but the chosen naturalist would be given a unique experience, as well as the honor and advantage of sharing the captain's cabin. Since FitzRoy was influential and well connected, and since the post would indeed be a prize for any naturalist, the offer was first made to people of some standing.

Henslow was one of these. He would have liked to have gone, but his wife looked so sad when he made the proposal that he gave up the idea. Another Cambridge man turned it down, regretfully, for reasons of health. Thoughts turned then to young Darwin; although not really a trained geologist, he was full of enthusiasm, with something of a flair—just the man for the job! So thought Darwin himself, though humbly enough. He recognized the offer for what it was, the chance of a lifetime.

It was, of course, great luck that he had been offered the post. But now befell the further chances and difficulties that so nearly prevented him from obtaining it. First of all, his family was surprisingly unenthusiastic. What, away from home two long years and even more! Worse, his father was definitely against the idea.

The young Charles was always apologetic and unsure of himself with his father. And here he was having to ask to be financially dependent on him for another two years or more. To Dr. Robert Darwin, the position must have been as clear as day. Here was his perverse, procrastinating, ne'er-do-well son merely repeating a performance and jibbing away from the *second* career chosen for him. It was useless for Charles to object that it would merely be a postponement of his clerical career and that the trip would broaden his outlook. His father didn't think so—more likely, it would introduce him to loose ways. In any case, the job couldn't be worth

Captain Robert FitzRoy, of the *Beagle*.

having if everyone was turning it down and they had to come to a man with no real training! Very regretfully, very sadly, Charles wrote a letter of refusal, *and* posted it.

Then, unexpectedly, came reprieve, or at least the possibility of reprieve. Relenting a little, his father announced that, if Charles could find "any man of common sense who advises you to go," he would give his consent. Charles's mind at once flew to his Uncle Josiah Wedgwood, and he rode across to see him.

There can be no doubt that by now Charles Darwin was inspiring confidence in his elders (though not yet, unfortunately, in his father) as a young man with "something about him." Uncle Jos was very definite in his opinion and in his estimation of what this voyage might do for his nephew. He took Charles straight back to Shrewsbury and together they spoke to Dr. Darwin. The parental decision was reversed. Charles, still mindful of the long-drawn expense that he was imposing on his father, ventured the remark that, anyway, he would have to be very clever to be able to spend much money on board ship. "But," answered his father with a smile, "they all tell me you *are* very clever!"

But would he perhaps be too late? Charles now began a feverish few days of driving about the countryside, hiring coaches, boarding the public express coach, "The Wonder," that over a distance of 240 miles could average as much as ten miles per hour. He dashed to Cambridge, to find the post still open; he dashed to London, for the all-important interview with Captain FitzRoy at the Admiralty.

That interview must have been a curious one. Captain FitzRoy had, after all, to live with the man that he chose at very close quarters for the next two years at least. He had, in the interval, heard something about Darwin from a mutual friend and seems to have been a little afraid of what he had been told of Charles's political opinions and of the chances of their not proving compatible. FitzRoy was, at the time, a keen student of the then popular "science" of phrenology, which sought to assess character from the shape of the head and features; and he at once, on seeing Darwin's nose, was struck with doubt as to the stability of character that it portrayed. He began to raise objections, to stress the disadvantages and discomforts of the voyage, even to suggest that, as a matter of fact, he had more or less offered the job to a friend, "a Mr. Chester, –er, Fletcher."

But Charles, by his patience and humility, by his enthusiasm and general likeableness, gradually wore away the objections and the feelings of criticism that FitzRoy was entertaining. The tone of the conversation began to veer; disabilities gave place to advantage; shapes of nose were forgotten, as well as the possibly mythical Mr. Chester Fletcher. The captain found himself expounding such practical details as that Darwin would need, of course, a good case of pistols; his own cost about £60. As for Charles, he came away from the interview, and an extension of it on the same evening, utterly delighted. He wrote to his sister that FitzRoy was his "*beau idéal* of a captain," and that the job was his. Would Nancy please make him twelve shirts, and "tell Edward to send me up in my carpet bag, my slippers, a pair of lightish walking shoes, my Spanish books, my new microscope, which must have cotton wool stuffed inside it, my geological compass, a little book if I have got it in my bedroom, *Taxidermy*." No more hesitation now for the young dilettante, no more jibbing; he had the bit between his teeth.

All this was, in fact, a little premature. There were delays, and Charles began to have second thoughts and qualms and fears of personal inadequacy, natural enough in the circumstances. His interview with FitzRoy was in early September—the September of 1831, so that Charles, while in London, had been able to witness the coronation procession of

King William IV—but the *Beagle* did not actually set out on
its long voyage until two days after Christmas.

One of Charles's first jobs was to go down to Plymouth
with FitzRoy to inspect the ship on which they were to sail.
They found the *Beagle* still mastless and in disorder, and
Charles was somewhat dismayed at the size of the vessel.
This ship that was to carry over sixty souls had a displace-
ment of only 235 tons, and its length was no more than 100
feet, with a breadth of 30 feet. A little disillusioned, Charles
returned home, made a round of farewell visits, and then set
out for London again, to make his final arrangements before
embarking on a voyage that he now heard might last as long

H.M.S. *Beagle* in the waters off Patagonia.

as four years. On October 23, he was on his way to Plymouth again to board the ship.

He met the officers, all young like their captain, and at first found them rather callow and comparable to the freshest of freshmen at Cambridge, though later he grew to like and admire them. He settled himself in his cabin and found that there was more room than he had expected, and that lack of space could be a blessing in disguise in that it imposed tidiness. All was intense activity, and, becoming infected with the prevailing excitement, he regained all of his previous enthusiasm. "She looks," he wrote to Henslow about his ship, "most beautiful, even a landsman must admire her. *We* all think her the most perfect vessel ever turned out of the Dockyard. . . . No vessel ever left England with such a set of chronometers, viz. twenty-four, all very good ones. In short, everything is well, and I have only now to pray for the sickness to moderate its fierceness, and I shall do very well."

Poor Charles was being sick as the *Beagle* rolled and wallowed in harbor. And the weather remained depressing, while an easterly wind, without which they could not leave port—a disadvantage of large sailing ships, now almost forgotten—would not materialize. He suffered from some form of eczema of the hands and from palpitations, the latter firmly convincing him that he had heart disease, though he carefully kept away from any doctor lest he should be prevented at the last minute from joining the expedition. At last, on December 10, the day seemed to have come. They cleared the harbor, but met a terrific storm and, after a wild twenty-four hours at sea, had to return. Charles had been terribly seasick and dragged himself back to lodgings in Devonport, where he made grim and rather desperate resolutions. "If," he confided to his diary, "I keep my health and return, and then have strength of mind quietly to settle down in life, my present and future share of vexation and want of comfort will be amply repaid. . . . If I have not energy enough to make myself steadily industrious during the voyage, how great and uncommon an opportunity of improving myself I shall throw away."

Christmas came, and still they were in harbor. The crew got roaring drunk. On the afternoon of December 27, they were really away, and Charles was watching the Eddystone lighthouse disappear below the horizon. On the next day, he was seasick again, while the captain was having the worst offenders in the Christmas debauch flogged. Supposing miser-

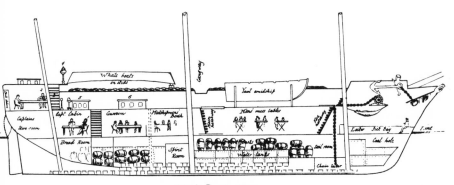

H.M.S. Beagle 1832

1 Mr Darwin's seat in Capt. Cabin
2 · · · · Poop ·
3 · · · · drawers · ·
4 Azimuth Compass
5 Captain's Skylight
6 Gunroom ·

A plan of the *Beagle*. The ship was officially described as a barque of 235 tons, belonging to the old class of 10-gun brigs.

ably that discipline had to be maintained, Darwin could not
help feeling that it was unfair to let the men get drunk and
then to punish them so brutally.

So, not auspiciously, began the famous voyage. The
voyage's official purpose was "to complete the Survey of Patagonia and Tierra del Fuego, commenced under Captain
King in 1826 to 1830; to survey the shores of Chile, Peru,
and of some islands in the Pacific; and to carry [for the
purpose of establishing exact longitude] a chain of chrono-
metrical measurements round the world." There was still
much of this sort of thing to do in 1832, and this was to be
an important voyage for the Royal Navy. There was still
much to be learned, however, in the fields of natural science
too—of the geological formation of distant coasts and islands, of both great and infinitesimally small plant and animal life, of sea and land and shore. The voyage could therefore be important scientifically. As for Darwin himself, "The
voyage of the *Beagle*," his autobiography unequivocally states,
"has been by far the most important event in my life and
has determined my whole career."

Of course, it need not have been so. If Darwin had been
the lazy, irresponsible character that his father had once
thought him to be—if he had let the inauspicious start, and
all the trying difficulties of living in so cramped and close
quarters, permanently dampen his spirits—he could have
gotten through the voyage giving adequate return for being
taken on it but with no real gain or contribution to science at
the end of it.

Not so, however! Darwin rose from his hammock of seasickness after the first few days and became such a dynamo
of energy as to fill the captain and officers with admiration

and wonder; to call him "steadily industrious" was an understatement. Trailing for marine specimens, dissecting and examining them on deck—a "damn beastly mess," the first lieutenant called them, but put up with it all—leaping ashore at every opportunity of an expedition, with Lyell's latest book almost literally in one hand and his little geological hammer in the other—Charles Darwin rapidly earned the admiring respect of his companions. They affectionately called him "the Flycatcher" or "the dear old Philosopher" and, in later years, were to pay tribute to his good temper and high spirits, as well as to his energy and industry.

With his ill health and doubts, but not his determination, forgotten and with great mental and physical gusto, the young Charles Darwin entered into his kingdom.

4

The Voyage of the Beagle

How MANY and varied were the discoveries that Charles Darwin made on his voyage! There were the days that he unearthed the fossil of the extinct megatherium in Patagonia and noticed its similarities to living mammals. There was the day that he quarreled with Captain FitzRoy about slavery—their politics were certainly not wholly compatible—and learned what an occasionally unreasonable, as well as at all times forceful, character his captain was. There was the shock of the first meeting with the Fuegian natives—were these creatures of the same species as himself? There was the earthquake, and the extraordinary variety of life on the Galápagos Islands. And there was the day—no, he was always to remember the very hour!—when he suddenly realized that he might have enough worthwhile material for none other than himself, Charles Darwin, to write a book! He was ambitious, but he was humble—as he was always to remain.

Let us follow the highlights of this round-the-world voyage of the *Beagle* that Darwin was, by a series of chances, lucky enough to make. Which of his experiences and discoveries helped to develop his later evolutionary theories, and in what ways, we will consider later; enough for the moment that there had started an important expedition.

This sailing was important for others besides Darwin. For Captain FitzRoy, rather more obviously than for his amateur passenger, it represented a crucial stage in his career, and FitzRoy had every intention of making the voyage a resounding success. It was important, too, for the three Fuegian natives on board and for their missionary companion.

This surprising cargo was, strangely, not mentioned by Darwin in his journal of the voyage until their restoration to their native land, when, however, he had a good deal to say of them. These three natives, given the picturesque names of Jemmy Button, Fuegia Basket, and York Minster, had been brought back to England from Tierra del Fuego by Captain FitzRoy on his earlier voyage. And now, after some efforts of education on their behalf in England, they were being returned, accompanied by a missionary named Matthews, so that they might teach their fellows the rudiments of civilization and Christianity, including better treatment than had been customary from any white seaman or whalers wrecked on their coasts.

The favorite on the voyage was Jemmy Button—so named because he was reputed to have been willingly exchanged by his parents for a button. "He was merry," says Darwin, "and often laughed, and was remarkably sympathetic with any-

one in pain; when the water was rough, I was often a little
seasick, and he used to come to me and say in a plaintive
voice, 'Poor, poor fellow!'; but the notion, after his aquatic
life, of a man being seasick, was too ludicrous, and he was
generally obliged to turn on one side to hide a smile or
laugh, and then he would repeat his 'Poor, poor fellow!' " If,
however, Darwin found these coffee-colored passengers little
more than amusing, he was to find their fellow-tribesmen in
their native haunts fascinating.

Seasickness did often lay Charles low, and from the start,
as we have seen. In fact, the first days, through the Bay of
Biscay, had been terrible. Only as they approached Tenerife
did the inexperienced young landsman recover. Then came a
disappointment. Permission to land on this beautiful island,
which Charles had always dreamed of visiting, was refused
from fear of cholera. Reward came ten days later, with a
three weeks' anchorage at the Cape Verde Islands. "Geologizing," Charles joyously exclaimed in a letter to his father—
really more to his sisters—"geologizing in a volcanic country
is most delightful; besides the interest attached to itself, it
leads you into most beautiful and retired spots. Nobody but
a person fond of Natural History can imagine the pleasure of
strolling under coconuts in a thicket of bananas and coffee-
plants, and an endless number of wild flowers." On horseback and on foot, with the purser and the assistant surgeon,
Charles explored the island and brought back to the ship for
examination plants, shells, corals, and the strange and ex-
quisite creatures of the seashore. By himself, he essayed his
first geological sketch map. He was learning rapidly as he
went along.

The voyage continued, and the ship crossed the equator
with the usual ceremonial horseplay. The days were hot

now, but the nights were cool and serene, and Charles paced the decks with contentment, if with an occasional qualm of homesickness—a feeling, incidentally, that was to increase to almost intolerable proportions before the long voyage was finished. On the morning of February 28, 1832, they sighted the South American coast and, on the same afternoon, they were tied up outside Bahía, or Salvador, Brazil's oldest city. FitzRoy found it smelly, but Darwin thought it beautiful and exciting. What really thrilled him, however, and what was always to excite him, was to walk in a tropical forest: "enough to make a florist go wild—nothing more nor less than a view in the Arabian Nights, with the advantage of reality."

But then came the quarrel with FitzRoy, in which Darwin was unjustly ranted at for calling his companion a liar, and which was all the more saddening because the captain had proved himself so sympathetic, kind, and altogether admirable. FitzRoy was overworked, Darwin decided, and he certainly had a quick and violent temper. The incident ended with a complete and handsome apology by the irascible and emotional captain. But, besides being, as was usual and proper, a little god on his own ship, FitzRoy was a very forceful personality; and Charles must have been careful thereafter to avoid getting on the wrong side of him, there being, in fact, only one further violent quarrel recorded during the voyage.

They set sail for the south again. The next incident was the excited shout, "Grampus bear to port!" Charles rushed up on deck: it was April Fool's Day! On April 4, they anchored in the magnificent harbor of Rio de Janeiro, there joining other British naval vessels. There followed some pleasant social occasions, and then a solid couple of months

GALAPAGOS
ARCHIPELAGO

Amazon River

A
N
D
E
S

Lima

Bahia

M
O
U
N
T
A
I
N
S

Concepción

Rio de Janeiro

River Plate

Valparaiso

Buenos Aires

Montevideo

Bahia Blanca

Punta Alta

SOUTH AMERICA

P
A
T
A
G
O
N
I
A

FALKLAND
ISLANDS

TIERRA
DEL FUEGO

CAPE HORN

Map of South America, showing the *Beagle*'s major ports of call on her voyage around the continent.

while the ship returned to Salvador and Charles was left behind in lodgings with time to explore, as he liked to do, on horseback and on foot. The variety and exuberance of tropical life greatly impressed him, as did its cruel competitiveness. A move father south followed, in July, to the mouth of the River Plate, which was to be the *Beagle*'s headquarters for the rest of its stay on South America's eastern coast.

The real adventure was now about to begin—the penetration into the wild and forbidding tip of South America, the Tierra del Fuego, where few white men had sailed and even fewer had landed. At its prospect the officers and crew allowed their beards to grow, Charles included. It started, however, a little surprisingly, with man-made and unlooked-for trouble, the *Beagle* becoming for a little while mixed up in local politics, revolutions, and wars. The ship was fired upon outside Buenos Aires, and its furious captain demanded, and received, an apology. Charles Darwin was just as furious.

A preliminary trip followed, as far south as Bahía Blanca (not to be confused with the first port of call, Bahía, or Salvador), on which Charles was allowed some time ashore and made the first of his discoveries of fossil mammals—which, however, were to be more than duplicated later in the year. Then, after a last taste of the sophisticated pleasures of civilization in Montevideo and Buenos Aires, in late November they pointed their prows finally for the southern tip of the land, the Horn, a little beyond which the relatives of Jemmy Button lived.

It was spring in those parts; but they were going toward a land where it was not always golden afternoon but, rather, one might say, leaden winter, with rain and winds and almost continuous heavy clouds—a gloomy land, which, how-

ever, did not prevent Charles Darwin, on viewing it, to
make, with a thrill, the vow of dedication that we quoted at
the beginning of this book.

This incident took place in the Bay of Good Success, beyond the Strait of Le Maire and not far from the famous and
stormbound Horn. On entering the bay, they had been
saluted by the waving of tattered cloaks and the long, sonor-
ous shouts of the native Fuegians. On the morrow, Captain
FitzRoy landed a party to communicate with them, and
Darwin was a member of the party:

> It was without exception the most curious and interesting
> spectacle I ever beheld: I could not have believed how wide
> was the difference between savage and civilized man; it is
> greater than between a wild and domesticated animal, inas-
> much as in man there is a greater power of improvement. The
> chief spokesman was old, and appeared to be the head of the
> family. . . .
>
> The old man had a fillet of white feathers tied round his
> head, which partly confined his black, coarse, and entangled
> hair. His face was crossed by two broad transverse bars; one,
> painted bright red, reached from ear to ear and included the
> upper lip; the other, white like chalk, extended above and
> parallel to the first, so that even his eyelids were thus col-
> oured. The other two men were ornamented by streaks of
> black powder. . . .
>
> Their very attitudes were abject, and the expression of their
> countenances distrustful, surprised, and startled.
>
> After we had presented them with some scarlet cloth, which
> they immediately tied round their necks, they became good
> friends. This was shown by the old man patting our breasts,
> and making a chuckling kind of noise, as people do when

feeding chickens. I walked with the old man, and this demonstration of friendship was repeated several times; it was concluded by three hard slaps, which were given me on the breast and back at the same time. He then bared his bosom for me to return the compliment, which being done, he seemed highly pleased.

Did Darwin reflect upon how different was the exchanging of amicable slaps with painted savages from an evening in the drawing room at Maer or the future life of a country clergyman? If he did, he added more constructive thoughts. A little later, he met some more of these Fuegians—of a tribe that did not hunt, but depended for a most precarious livelihood upon fishing and combing the beaches for whatever sustenance they could find there. They were a more stunted and, it seemed to him, a more degraded type. Then, at length, the three who had made their journey to England were put ashore, and Darwin marveled at the utter lack of demonstrativeness on the part of all the natives concerned.

He noticed their phenomenal powers of mimicry. Was this "a consequence of the more practised habits of perception and keener senses, common to all men in a savage state, as compared with those long civilized?" But, for the rest—what abject and miserable creatures! "Viewing such men, one can hardly make oneself believe that they are fellow creatures, and inhabitants of the same world." Yet they manifestly were; and they manifestly extracted some pleasure from their way of existence or they would not continue with it. But, "what could have tempted, or what change compelled a tribe of men, to leave the fine regions of the north, to travel down the Cordillera, or backbone of America, to invent and

One of the Fuegian natives who so intrigued Darwin. This illustration
was included in the book Darwin wrote after the voyage.

build canoes, which are not used by the tribes of Chile,
Peru, and Brazil, and then to enter on one of the most inhos-
pitable countries within the limits of the globe?" Whatever
the reason, "Nature, by making habit omnipotent, and its
effects hereditary, has fitted the Fuegian to the climate and
the productions of his miserable country."

Now, Charles was to have over twelve months of varied adventures, sometimes with his shipmates, more often away from them, while Captain FitzRoy continued his surveying, sailing up and down the coast and across to the Falkland Islands. There was often real danger to be met, as well as hard conditions, something that should not be forgotten when we come to contemplate the long years—sedentary, uneventful, and valetudinarian—of Darwin's later life. The expedition to dump the three Fuegians had had to be made away from the *Beagle* and in small whaleboats; and, one day, a great fall of ice from the cliffs above caused such a wave as would have swept their boats away had not Darwin and some others rushed to the rescue. Then, he went for long expeditions on horseback across the plains of Patagonia in the company of Gauchos, or cowboys.

Darwin liked the Gauchos. One day, he imitated their use of the bolas, a contraption of rope and three heavy balls that the practiced horseman threw from the saddle to entangle the feet of the animal that he wished to ensnare. Unluckily, one of the balls hit a bush and proceeded to entangle Charles's own horse. "The Gauchos roared with laughter; they cried out that they had seen every sort of animal caught, but never before seen a man caught by himself." More seriously, there was the ever-present need to protect themselves from marauding Indians, made fierce by the determined efforts being made at that time to exterminate them. Charles spent three days in the camp of the infamous Colonel Rosas, who was directing this extermination campaign, and had time to wonder at the court that this extraordinary man held—he even kept a couple of buffoons, like a

medieval baron. Darwin was able to note the contrast between the Fuegians and the men of the one Indian tribe that
Rosas had duped into becoming his ally.

More than once Darwin returned to Punta Alta, near
Bahía Blanca, the place he had found to be "a perfect catacomb
for monsters of extinct races." His finds were considerable
and, to him, very intriguing. Mostly, they were of different
varieties of the megatherium, or giant sloth. Some of its
bony plates had a marked resemblance to those of the still
existing armadillo; indeed, there were many resemblances to
existing animals. Then there was the toxodon, which Darwin thought related to the present-day sea cow, or manatee,
and which seemed a wonderful blend of several different
modern orders of animal. Finally, he discovered the tooth of
an ancient horse, an animal understood to have been intro-
duced into America no more than 300 years ago: what had
led to its previous extinction?

A year passed, and they returned to the scene of the
dumping of the three Fuegians. Already, that strange project
had proved semitragic. The missionary Matthews had to be
taken off the island after a trial stay of a few weeks and after
he had received the most harassing, not to say degrading,
treatment and had seemed in danger of his life. There
seemed, at first, no trace of their one-time friends at all; but
then a near-naked and painted savage came rowing out to
them. It was Jemmy Button, sadly reverted to his former
state. He had not forgotten all of his English, and ate a
hearty meal with the captain and Darwin, complaining bit-
terly that York Minster and Fuegia Basket had robbed him
of all his possessions and left him, but finally asserting dog-
gedly that he did not wish to be taken back on board. Fitz-
Roy was saddened by the final outcome of his philanthropic

experiment, as well he might be. Charles no doubt kept his thoughts to himself, but recorded in his journal the loyal and pious hope that more good would prove to have been done than harm. "When Jemmy reached the shore he lighted a signal fire, and the smoke curled up, bidding us a last and long farewell, as the ship stood on her course into the open sea."

Within a few months, H.M.S. *Beagle* was at last leaving the gloomy coasts of Tierra del Fuego and making for the Pacific Ocean. Two and one-half years had gone by since it had set sail from Plymouth Sound; there were nearly another two and one-half years to go.

5

*The Voyage
Continued*

Now FOR the Andes, the Cordillera, the mighty backbone of
South America, down which those strange primitives the
Fuegians had once trekked. Charles the geologist looked
forward to them with enthusiasm; so did the rest of the
officers and crew, for that matter, for all were heartily sick of
the rain and damp and everlasting pall of clouds of the
Patagonian peninsula.

They had indeed had a sight of these Andes mountains
and had already penetrated at least to their base. For Captain FitzRoy had ordained, as a final task on the eastern side
of their voyage, an exploration up the Santa Cruz River,
which had never before been traversed by a white man farther than some thiry miles up its estuary.

It was another of those whaleboat expeditions that only a young and fit man could have faced and in which Darwin delighted. Here the river's current was surprisingly strong, and the only mode of progress was to tow the boats from the bank. This was a job at which all took a turn, as they did in guarding the camp at night against marauding Indians. Signs of Indians were met, but no more, which disappointed Charles, who had surmised that they would be "out and out wild gentlemen." He shot a condor, however, that measured eight feet from wing to wing, trapped and observed a distinctive species of mouse, and replenished the common larder by bringing down with his gun some guanaco, or wild llama.

After the best part of three weeks, the river took an unexpected turn from west to south, and, since the food supply was beginning to run short, FitzRoy decided to return. Most considered the expedition a waste of time. But Darwin was fascinated by the geological signs that he was able to read. The river valley, for instance, was one vast pebble bed, as much as 200 miles across and 50 feet deep, "derived from the slow falling masses of rock on the old coast-lines and banks of rivers." What colossal changes in the face of the earth it was possible to witness; what staggering passages of time—passages that made Bishop Ussher's "4004 B.C." seem childish—must have been passed in the earth's history! "Catastrophes" were not needed as an explanation of life's history, but one long, sufficiently long, stupendously long, gradualism. Charles, always cheered, as who would not be, by his own powers of observation and his discoveries, was in high spirits; the time of the evening meal around the great fire he described as "merry."

They passed through the Straits of Magellan, and now became sad. Here the purser died, having suffered some time from unexplained illnesses, and was buried at sea. He was not the first companion to whom they had had to say good-bye.

Valparaíso, however, and clear skies cheered their spirits, though not the captain's. Now, in fact, FitzRoy suffered a nervous breakdown. He had been working incredibly hard; he had been spending his own money with rash liberality in anticipation of Admiralty support, and now found that they considered his schemes too ambitious. Fearing for his own sanity, he resigned in favor of the first lieutenant, and the immediate prospect changed to one of a prompt return home. Charles, for all his homesickness, was appalled and planned a sixteen-month schedule on his own. The captain was persuaded to change his mind, however, and to take over command again. Everyone, Darwin not least, was relieved—paradoxically so, because FitzRoy now decided to curtail his program, and a final end to the expedition, which had begun to appear interminable, came in sight. Charles immediately put in hand schemes for crossing the Andes.

But, first, he suffered and witnessed a major earthquake. He was ashore in the tropical forest with his personal servant—FitzRoy did not allow anyone to wander on shore alone. He was lying down when suddenly the earth rocked and swayed beneath him; it was a sensation, he wrote afterward, akin to that experienced when skating over thin ice. The leaves of the trees whispered strangely. He leaped to his feet, and the shuddering motion made him giddy. He guessed that great damage would have been done in nearby Concepción.

Soon they all saw the damage. The cathedral was a ruin. Quite truly, not one house had been left inhabitable. A heavy death toll had been averted only because the shock had come in the morning when most people were out of their houses. It was the force of the shock that impressed Darwin: "the ground is traversed by rents, the solid rocks are shivered, solid buttresses six to ten feet thick are broken into fragments like so much biscuit." However appalled he was by the disaster, he could not help exulting in having seen it. How much better to witness the wonders of nature, the changes that the face of the earth could suffer, than merely to read about them! "It is one of the three most interesting spectacles," he wrote to his sister, a little naïvely and detachedly, "I have beheld since leaving England—a Fuegian savage; tropical vegetation; and the ruin of Concepción."

Soon, in his enthusiasm, he was addressing his family in his letters home like a lecturer on the platform. "You are aware that plants of Arctic regions are frequently found in lower latitudes at an elevation which produces an equal degree of cold. I noticed a rather curious illustration of this law," and, in the same letter, "What is of much greater consequence, I have procured fossil shells (from an elevation of 12,000 ft.)." He adds, "But I am afraid you will tell me I am prosy with my Geological descriptions and theories"; though that fear did not stop him from telling someone, even if it was only his sister 8,000 miles away. These Andes mountains, he realized, had once been the floor of the sea, and they were the result of a comparatively recent upheaval; he was observing important facts in nothing less than "the theory of the formation of the world." He also mentions in this letter that, in one part of his trip over the Andes, he had to traverse a distance of a day and one-half's journeying where no water of any sort was available and that, having become "freckled" with fleabites, he had learned that it was preferable to sleep out in the open than in a native hut. To his father he declared that the expedition had been highly successful, but, he was afraid, highly expensive—two Peons (native peasants)and ten mules had accompanied him.

At length, the *Beagle* turned from the coasts of South America and set sail for the Galápagos archipelago, that group of volcanic, lava-strewn islands that lies some 500 miles to the west of the continent and almost exactly on the equator.

Their first sight of the islands was not encouraging; someone likened the view to that of the more cultivated parts of Hell. Nevertheless, there was much to interest the inquiring mind of a naturalist.

Charles considered the giant tortoises. He timed their walk —60 yards in 10 minutes; say, four miles a day. He sat on their backs, gave their shells a whack, and found it hard to keep his balance. He observed that they never seemed to die of old age. The great, ugly lizards on the rocky shores, three to four feet long, he found very curious. By opening a specimen's stomach he established their diet to be a seaweed not to be found on the shore; yet, they had a rooted objection to being pushed into the sea when they did not want to go there. He spent some interesting hours throwing one into the sea and waiting for it to come back, always without delay and to the same place—an inherited instinct, he presumed, to avoid as much as possible an element full of its enemies. He watched the yellow land lizard making its earth burrow. He approached one with its head well inside and pulled its tail. "At this it was greatly astonished, and soon shuffled up to see what was the matter; and then stared me in the face, as much as to say, 'What made you pull my tail?'" This animal had been created, he thought, in the center of the archipelago and had spread from there.

The birds he found almost idiotically tame. The finches he observed in particular, since over the various islands they possessed a great variety of beaks, in a perfect gradation of size from one as large as that of a hawfinch to that of a chaffinch: "one might really fancy that from an original paucity of birds in this archipelago, one species had been taken and modified for different ends." In fact, each different island was to a considerable extent inhabited by a different set of creatures, not altogether different, of course, but just a little. The governor of the island told him that, for instance, he could tell from which island a giant tortoise came, merely by looking at it. This was something that, he confessed, he had never dreamed of. But it was a fact, he also confessed in his journal, to which he did not for some time pay much attention.

Charles would have liked to stay longer on these strange islands. But they had the rest of the world to traverse, and they moved on. They visited Tahiti and continued on to New Zealand. There they said good-bye to Matthews, the missionary who had failed to establish himself on Tierra del Fuego. They moved on to Australia, and Darwin was naturally interested in the aborigines; he considered them superior to the Fuegians, but noted that their members were dwindling with the curtailment of their natural food supply.

Charles was growing tired, however, as they were all growing tired. They were sated with sights and new experiences. The prevailing thought was: every mile is a mile nearer home. This did not prevent one last important discovery, however. Charles, while aesthetically delighted at the sight of a coral island in the center of its calm reef-protected lagoon, was interested in how such a curious formation had ever come to pass. The accepted theory was that of a pushing up above the surface of old volcano tops. Charles, noting that coral could not live and form more than a few feet below the sea's surface, and arguing that, if the Andes mountains had been pushed up so high, then the nearby Pacific probably had been and was being correspondingly pushed down, put forward a theory that was the complete opposite of the currently accepted one (see diagram). He was, when he reached home, to have the satisfaction of witnessing his great teacher in geology, Charles Lyell, dance around the room with joy at the neatness, simplicity, and obvious rightness of the theory that was supplanting his own. Well on the way home, at Ascension Island, he was also cheered by a letter from his sister telling him that the famous Sedgwick had written to his late headmaster: "He is doing admirable work in South America and has already sent home a collection above all price."

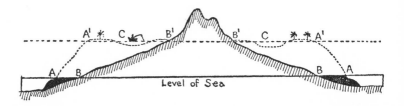

Section taken from Darwin's journal showing formation of a coral island with a barrier reef around it. The black patches at AB and BA, on the line of the original sea level, show coral formed where sea and land met. After the island subsides, the coral will keep pace with subsidence by continuing to grow upward. Its head will be just at the level of the water, thus forming a reef. (New coral is shown by the two points A^1 and the new sea level is designated by a dotted line.) The island is now smaller (point B^1 to B^1), and there is a lagoon between it and the coral reef (see two points C).

That delicious praise must have softened the blow now administered by FitzRoy, who announced that he was cutting across the southern Atlantic, once more, to South America in order to complete his chronological data. A final farewell, therefore, to South American tropical scenery, to be remembered "like a tale heard in childhood, a picture full of indistinct but most beautiful figures," and in autumn, 1836, by way of the Azores, Darwin was really steering a course for England and home.

On Sunday, October 2, after a storm up the Channel, they were tying up at Falmouth, and Charles was at once asking for coaches to the north. Through the hills and woods and fields of Gloucester and Worcester and, at last, his own Shropshire, he wondered that his fellow passengers could sit so stolid. He reached Shrewsbury by midnight of October 4; not wishing to disturb his family, he slept at an inn. Next morning, just before breakfast, he rushed in unannounced. The girls exclaimed that he was thinner. His father said: "Why, the shape of his head is quite altered!"

6

Q.E.D.

CHARLES MUST have felt different as well as looked it. He did, indeed, take the remark by his father, whose powers of observation he rated highly, as a significant indication of change. Was he then going to settle down to his intended career as a clergyman?

This prospect troubled him for awhile, for he no longer felt in the least fitted for the vocation. But neither his father nor anybody else seemed now to expect him to enter the Church; and the subject was tacitly dropped, never to be seriously brought up again. In his old age, Darwin merely reflected that some German phrenologist had said that his bump of reverence was highly developed, so perhaps he had missed his vocation after all!

He was tremendously busy. He found himself now fully accepted into the scientific community. There were friends and colleagues—new ones and old—to meet, not least among them his great master in geology, Lyell, whom he found both impressive and wholly delightful. He was asked to give lectures. He became a member of the Geological, Geographical, and Zoological associations, and soon was the busy secretary of the first of these. There was much writing, publishing, and editing to be faced, for not only was he to write one of the three official journals of the voyages of the *Beagle*, but also some strictly scientific publications on his zoological specimens—he had sent a mass of these home— were to be brought out at government expense, and, although he did not write these, he edited them. In fact, if he had come home not to find himself famous, he had at least returned to find himself deeply involved. He set about his tasks with characteristic thoroughness.

For the most part, he was working in London, which he found dirty, foggy, and uncongenial. The palpitations that had frightened him as he waited to sail from Plymouth returned to worry him. It was not all work and no play, however, and rumors began flitting between his sisters at Shrewsbury and his Wedgwood cousins at Maer that he was thinking of becoming engaged to a girl in London.

Charles was, in fact, thinking of marrying. He considered the subject with scientific detachment and seriousness. The results of his cogitations have, by chance, come down to us—they are the efforts not so much of a prig but of a serious-minded young man used to putting thoughts down on paper as an aid to consideration, and with the saving grace of being able to laugh at himself at the same time. First came some notes on the wider question of what he should do with his life. Travel? That depended on his health and vigor and "how far I become zoological." Not travel then, but "work at transmission of Species—microscope—simplest forms of life—geology. . . ?" Or take "a small house in Regent's Park—keep horses—take summer tours . . . systematize and study affinities?" Or try to become a Cambridge Professor —"and make the best of it"? That last prospect obviously did not please him very much, and, in any case, all these choices were affected by whether he married or not. And so, carefully, in double columns, he put down for his own consideration:

MARRY	Not MARRY
Children—(if it please God)— constant companion (friend in old age) who will feel interested in one, object to be beloved and played with—better than a dog anyhow—Home, and someone to take care of house—Charms of music and female chit-chat. These things good for one's health. Forced to visit and receive relations *but terrible loss of time.*	No children (no second life), no one to care for one in old age.—What is the use of working without sympathy from near and dear friends—who are near and dear friends to the old except relatives? Freedom to go where one liked—Choice of Society *and little of it.* Conversation of clever men at clubs.
My God, it is intolerable to think of spending one's whole life; like a neuter bee, working, working and nothing after all. —No, no won't do.—Imagine living all one's day solitarily in	Not forced to visit relatives, and to bend in every trifle— to have the expense and anxiety of children—perhaps quarrelling. *Loss of time*—cannot read in the evenings—fatness and idleness—anxiety and responsibility

smoky dirty London House.— Only picture to yourself a nice soft wife on a sofa with good fire, and books and music perhaps—compare this vision with the dingy reality of Gt Marlboro' St [brother Erasmus' rooms] Marry—Marry—Marry. Q.E.D. —less money for books, etc.— if many children forced to gain one's bread.—(But then it is very bad for one's health to work too much.) Perhaps my wife won't like London; then the sentence is banishment and degradation with indolent idle fool—

Obviously, the attractions of marriage won the day in spite of "terrible loss of time," and on the back of the scrap of paper were further cogitations: "It being proved necessary to marry—When? Soon or Late?" The only logical answer was soon rather than late; so, "Never mind my boy— cheer up—One cannot live the solitary life, with groggy old age, friendless and old and childless staring one in one's face, already beginning to wrinkle. Never mind, trust to chance—keep a sharp look out.—There is many a happy slave—"

Charles did not really have to keep much of a sharp look out, one feels; his destiny was waiting for him, although perhaps he did not yet really know it, and this was not in the shape of the unknown young lady in London. He found himself attracted to Maer, as he always did, and attracted in particular to Emma, the gay, kindly, highly intelligent youngest daughter of Uncle Jos, whose accomplishments included in marked degree the usual Victorian one of pianoplaying—she had had lessons from Chopin—as well as the more unexpected one of archery. On one visit, he dared not pop the question; but, in November, 1838, he did—and was accepted.

The next year, January 29, 1839, Charles and Emma were married, and found themselves a house on Gower Street, in Bloomsbury—a German bomb destroyed the house in 1941 —settling down with as much work as possible for Charles and some entertaining by Emma. Sedgwick, the Henslows, and the Lyells were visitors. Tea was taken with the Fitz-Roys: the captain had married and there was a little FitzRoy already; but Charles, who always admired the man intensely, found his one-time *beau idéal* even more prickly and opinionated than ever and rather difficult to get on with, even for an afternoon. Charles had had read to him some of

Emma and Charles Darwin in 1840, from water-color portraits by George Richmond.

the journal of the earlier voyage of the *Beagle*, mostly written by the Captain King from whom FitzRoy had taken over. He found it dull, which indeed it is, Charles's own volume being easily the most readable, though parts of FitzRoy's narrative in the second volume run a close second.

The task of entertaining in his London house Darwin took very seriously; and he found that it exhausted him. In fact, he was finding that many things now exhausted him. His health was not good, and it was growing worse; it seems almost to have grown worse immediately, or at any rate soon, after he married, as if he were unconsciously throwing himself back with relief on the kindly and patient adminis-trations—and she was kindly and patient, and had need to be—of his wife.

This illness of Charles Darwin's, which continued inter-mittently but without real letup for the rest of his life, is a curious business. He suffered from bouts of sickness, in-somnia, giddiness, and general debility that for days pre-vented him from leaving the house and even from doing any work. Was it the aftereffects of his long and often quite terrible bouts of seasickness on the *Beagle*? It may have been. Was it a nervous and psychological malady, the result of a repressed childhood and an overbearing father? It may have been. Was it an unconsciously assumed protection against going out to attend functions that he did not wish to attend—against, in his later life, facing the opposition that his writings were to create? There may well have been some-thing of that. He himself, at the end of his autobiography, admitted that, "even ill-health, though it has annihilated several years of my life, has saved me from the distractions of society and amusement," which, however, is not quite the same thing.

Whatever the cause, Charles was finding his health badly impaired, and grimy Victorian London sadly disagreeable to it. The obvious solution was a house in the country and a retirement thereto, which might mean a retirement also from the struggle to succeed in a scientific career, an acknowledgment that "the race was to the strong" and that he was not of that breed. After a great deal of trouble, a house was found at the village of Down, near Bromley, in Kent—a big, pleasant, rambling house with large grounds, which still exists and has now been partly turned into a Darwin museum. There, in 1842, already with a family of two, the Darwins moved. Charles did much to improve the property, and planted for himself a tree-lined walk. And, there, he walked and contemplated until, forty years later, he died.

Charles, in fact, at this time suddenly seems to have become a different man—it would be absurd to say an old man, but certainly a middle-aged man. Five years of adventure—and it *was* adventure, around the world with the *Beagle*, often very tough adventure—were now to be followed by forty years of work and thought.

Work, certainly; but when, the reader may begin to ask, is Darwin's life work, the great discoveries and theories in the world of organic evolution, going to begin? That is a question that even at the time some of his friends—some of those few, that is to say, who were privy to the secret of where his interests really lay—were beginning to ask themselves.

The first hint, tentative and hidden, came in his book, published in 1842, the year of his move to Down House, that had the rather forbiddingly long title *The Structure and Distribution of Coral Reefs: Being the First Part of the Geology of the Voyage of the "Beagle."* It was a book, he complained later, that had cost him twenty months of labor over three and a half years, the least productive period of his scientific life. It painstakingly surveyed all the Pacific coral formations and clearly and fully set out his theory of their evolution. It showed the author's powers of marshaling and linking facts and of drawing generalized conclusions from them; it showed his willingness to face all possible objections and of satisfactorily disposing of them. In such very general ways, it foreshadowed *The Origin of Species.* But, for those gifted with some insight and those who read the concluding paragraphs of the book, there might well appear a hint as to which way the wind of Charles's interests was blowing. It was not the subsidence of the ocean bed that interested him, but its effects upon life, animal life. Whether or not a particular area of the world's surface was a rising or a subsiding area, he said, "will directly bear upon that most mysterious question—whether the series of organized beings peculiar to some isolated points are the last remnants of a former population or the first creatures of a new race springing into existence."

"Springing into existence," we may note; not "created."

7

Mutability and Barnacles

"MUTABILITY" IS a slightly unfamiliar word. It means no more and no less than changeability, ability to change, liability to change, coming as it does from the Latin verb *mutare*, to change or move. It is a neater word than any of its more strictly English equivalents, and Darwin and his contemporaries were using it. Darwin, of course, was not only using it but thinking about it a great deal. To others it was still anathema—"The accursed thing," something not to be contemplated, since everyone knew that species had been created as they were, and it was sacrilegious to think otherwise.

That was the crux of the matter. And so we come to another term needing careful definition, "species"; for this is essentially a scientific chapter. Again we have a Latin word,

meaning originally something seen, an image, an appearance, a *kind* of thing—we use the word thus loosely in English: he was driving a strange contraption, some ancient
species of motorcar. In biology it is more specific: the final
and fundamental division of life, whether animal or vegetable, coming below Genus, Family, Order, etc. (see Glossary,
under ORDER). It is, in fact, not easily definable with exactness, but a very good approximation is "a group of *interbreeding* individuals, *not* interbreeding with another such group."
To an ordinary person a species of animal is a *kind* of animal;
and he really is not far wrong.

When did Charles Darwin begin to believe that species
were mutable and not immutable? To be quite candid, he
must have grown up with the idea. It was, as we have seen,
one of his grandfather Erasmus' ideas, and also one of the
French naturalist Lamarck. But it is one thing to be familiar
with an idea, an idea that no orthodox or accepted scientist
was allowing himself to entertain, and another thing to believe in it. Further, it is one thing to believe in an idea and
another to be able to prove that it is correct. Here, we shall
consider Charles's reaction to his grandfather's poem *Zoonomia*, with all its startling footnotes.

The reaction is stated adequately in his autobiography: he
admired *Zoonomia* greatly when he read it in his youth;
"but on reading it a second time after an interval of ten or
fifteen years, I was much disappointed, the proportion of
speculation being so large to the facts given." In other
words, *guesswork*; and that was a thing that was anathema
to Charles Darwin, a method entirely alien to his nature.
The greatest sin of all, in his estimation, was to theorize and
generalize without an adequate foundation of facts. Had not

the poet Samuel Coleridge, after reading Erasmus Darwin's book, claimed wild theorizing to be synonymous with "Darwinizing"? That was something to avoid, indeed to live down.

This second of the Darwin biologists, therefore, Charles Darwin, both from warning example and from natural predilection, was going to proceed very slowly indeed.

However, it is obvious that, from the very start of his famous voyage, Charles's mind was *attuned* to the idea of the mutability of species and that, by the end of it, he had collected such evidence as to make the idea stare him immovably in the face. There is also one minor factor that has not even been mentioned in our description of the voyage. Captain FitzRoy was a "diehard" in this matter and grew increasingly so, going out of his way in his published volume about the voyage to suggest evidence of the strict truth of the Bible's creation stories and castigating doubters with such observances as that it was foolish to question the ability of God to make the lion lie down with the lamb within the confines of the Ark, more particularly since all the animals would in any case be thoroughly cowed by the fact of the Deluge. We know how forthright and forceful a character FitzRoy was, and this sort of thing must have had an irritating and stimulating effect upon Charles. For there is nothing more warranted to strengthen us in entertaining a new idea than to see other people making fools of themselves, as we consider, in holding an old one.

Some of the phenomena that during the voyage of the *Beagle* turned Darwin's mind toward considering evolutionary theories have been stated, or rather, perhaps, hinted at, in the course of describing the voyage. Now we will state them categorically, with their implications. Reduced to the bare minimum they are really quite simple.

(1) It became obvious to Darwin, firstly, that the earth was incredibly old; secondly, that it had suffered many and continuous changes to the nature of its surface; and, thirdly, that, as Lyell put it, the changes that the earth had suffered were no different from the processes of change that were still going on.

(2) This changing surface of the earth was life's environment. And as that environment changed, life *adapted* itself to the change. Even the part of life that was human life adapted itself to environment—witness the Fuegians.

(3) Different environments consequently produced different types of life, types that *fitted* that environment. Further, the process had been going on in the past, for millions of years. And, in particular, if an environment became isolated, the types of life that fitted it would become isolated and, thus, highly distinctive. That had probably happened, on a large scale, on the Australian continent, with its peculiar type of mammal, the marsupial; it perhaps had happened on a small scale in the islands of the Galápagos archipelago, where, most curiously, the fauna—the birds, in particular—were at one and the same time similar to those on the South American mainland and yet, in small degrees, distinctive to *each* island.

(4) In the course of time, many animals, as the fossils of Punta Alta showed, had become extinct. But those animals, in their anatomy, in what might be called their general ground plan, were remarkably like animals that still existed. There was, in fact, a *continuity*.

Exactly how far, by the end of the voyage, Darwin had

reached in propounding to himself the theory of evolution
that was to make him famous, it is really not possible to tell.
It is at least certain that he did not *start* the voyage with the
idea. Lyell, whose writings he so admired, while stressing
the age of the earth and the idea of continuity, remained
strictly orthodox on the immutability of species; and the
very fact that grandfather Erasmus had speculated so airily
and irresponsibly was likely, if anything, to sway Charles
toward orthodoxy too.

What is also certain, however, is that the evolutionary
idea was perpetually nagging at Darwin and that, in the
process of writing up his journal of the voyage, the nagging
became more persistent than ever. In 1837, he started a first
notebook on facts and comments bearing on the mutation of
species. Here, he felt, was, at the least, something that
should be looked into, once the job of the journal was out of
the way.

By February, 1838, the first notebook was filled and another immediately started. Already, he had gone far in speculation—and Charles did not despise speculation, he loved
it, in fact; what he did not condone was the publicizing of
such speculation without sufficient proof to back it. "If we
choose to let conjecture run wild," he had even dared to jot
down, "then animals, our fellow brethren in pain, disease,
death, suffering and famine—our slaves in the most labori-
ous works, our companions in our amusement—they may
partake of our origin in our common ancestry—we may all
be melted together." He knew perfectly well that he was
putting forward a profoundly startling, but also a most important, proposition. Soon the notebook expanded to a series
of folders kept in his study. About this time he read and was
much impressed by a book by a clergyman and economist

named Thomas R. Malthus, with the title *An Essay on the Principle of Population*—of which more later. Then, finally, in 1842, when he had gotten his Coral Reef book out of the way, he went so far as to put an outline of his theories down in writing—thirty-odd pages of penciled notes.

This he put away, and told no one where he had put it. But, two years later, he was to take it out again and expand it to a carefully written exposition of 189 pages. He then attached to it a letter to his wife, instructing her to have it published "in case of my sudden death, as my most solemn and last request, which I am sure you will consider the same as if legally entered in my will." The help of a competent editor—Lyell or Henslow, for instance—was to be enlisted in preparing it for publication. Charles now had no doubt that what he had written was of importance. But that was a very different matter from considering it ready for publication—no "Darwinizing" for him! If God gave him the strength and the time, there was a great deal of work he must do before he would consider the theory really ready to face the critical and, as he was sure, unfriendly eyes of the world.

As a start, Darwin found himself embarked on a work that was to demand most of his attention for nothing less than the next eight years. And it all began with a little creature that he had brought back from the voyage and that was not much bigger than the head of a pin.

It was not until 1846 that all the scientific books resulting from his research during the voyage of the *Beagle* were finally published and he had prepared a revised edition of the more popular *Journal of Researches*.* There remained

---

* Originally published in 1839, this account brought him in the first literary profits that he made; however, he had adequate private means, to be increased at his father's death in 1848.

only one thing left over from the voyage to which he thought he might give attention, a tiny cirriped ("fringed-foot"), or barnacle, which had intrigued him by its uncommon features. He thought he might write a short monograph about it and its significance. It would involve some further research, of course, some comparison between it and more ordinary barnacles, but the job needed doing; indeed, what really needed doing—and all his scientific friends were agreed upon this—was that the whole business of the classification of the cirripeds should be tackled afresh and placed on a sound footing.

So Charles Darwin found himself drawn into a task that grew larger and larger as he became immersed. He went into it, however, with his eyes open. It would be, he felt, practical training and the sort of training that he needed—dissecting, making slides, peering into the microscope, finding out all there was to find out about one particular set of animal species. It would be delightful work too, using "eyes and fingers again," rather than perpetually finding the right word and spinning sentences together, a job Darwin never found easy, although he was always a clear and often a striking writer.

Darwin asked his new friend Joseph Hooker what he thought about the barnacle project. Hooker, a younger man who had also been on an expedition as a naturalist and was a most enthusiastic admirer of Darwin, agreed entirely. One had hardly the right to theorize about species in general, he observed, if one had never minutely described any. Several years later, Hooker was rashly expressing to Darwin his wish that his friend were back on his evolutionary studies—a remark that drew from Darwin the rejoinder "this is too bad of you!" Barnacles and species, the affronted naturalist explained, really ran together. Had he not been the first to discover a barnacle that, contrary to the usual run, was not hermaphrodite or self-fertilizing, but had two little pockets in the valves of her shell "in each of which she kept a little husband?" And had not, then, his theory of the *mutability* of species helped him to understand that here indeed was a gradual change taking place, from a unisexual to a bisexual creature? "Do not flatter yourself," he wrote gaily to Hooker, "that I shall not yet live to finish the Barnacles, and then make a fool of myself on the subject of species!"

There, of course, lay the serious trouble; Darwin *was* afraid of making a fool of himself. He was afraid too, it seems probable, of hurting the feelings of those he liked and admired and those who had deeply influenced him—Captain FitzRoy, for instance, and his own father. And so the years marched on, and he published four books on barnacles; it even came to such a pitch that one of his young children could ask of a friend, "and where does *your* Daddy do his barnacles?" Darwin's growing family also, of course, took up some of his time, for he was a good and loving father. There were the usual childish illnesses, less controllable in those days—whooping cough and the like—and the going away for holidays or the renting of a house in London for awhile, in order to bring everyone back to health. One little girl, Annie, did not recover and died at the age of ten, to the great grief of her parents.

These were the years, too, of Charles's own worst health. Tenderly nursed by his wife, he became for awhile really a confirmed invalid, something of which, in fact, he always remained. Even the contemplation of a task or a journey— one cannot help feeling, particularly a *disliked* task or journey—upset him.

Even in health, he led the quietest and most careful of lives. Here is the almost invariable program of his days. Up early and a short walk before breakfast. Breakfast alone, and then work at his desk from 8 to 9:30 A.M. Next, an hour's rest lying on the sofa, reading his correspondence or listening to his wife reading her family letters. Then another hour or two's work, followed invariably by a walk around the grounds or farther afield with his dog, watching the children play, examining his experimental seeds and plants, observing nature. The only variation was the riding of a placid pony instead of the use of his own two legs. After lunch, back to the sofa again, to read the newspaper. Then he wrote his own letters. Then up to his bedroom couch, to smoke and to listen to his wife reading to him—he was sorry if he sometimes fell asleep, because Emma would go on with the book lest the cessation of her voice wake him. Another short walk, an hour's work if he felt up to it, a little more of being read to perhaps, and then dinner at 7:30. After dinner, a game of backgammon with Emma perhaps, the reading of some scientific book or paper, a quiet and happy listening while Emma played the piano. Bed at 10:30, and the hope that tonight he would sleep well.

An irritating man, a man to lose patience with? But his wife did not find him so. Certainly a different man from the tough young enthusiast who had crossed the Cordillera and ridden day-long with the Gauchos. Yet not wholly, not fundamentally, different. Darwin was still working, as he had always worked after the reprehensible easygoing semi-idleness of Cambridge, as hard as he knew how to and as he believed he could work.

Nor did Darwin ever lose sight of the wider purpose behind all this self-imposed research into barnacles. He was not entirely a recluse. He traveled even so far afield as Glasgow—there were trains in which you could "steam" about the landscape now—to attend the annual conference of the British Association. He met Thomas Huxley, who later was to become his champion. He also met Alfred Russel Wallace, who had traveled in the Amazonian forests, had read with attention Darwin's *Beagle* journal, and was also interested in the mutability of species.

At length, in 1854, the long preoccupation with barnacles was over, the last scientific book about them was written, and the borrowed specimens were packed up and returned. Now, better trained, better equipped, in better health, Darwin could return to his real love. "Hurrah"—as he had prematurely observed to a friend two or three years back— "hurrah for species work!"

After all, when he really came to think of it, he might, with his poor health, die before he had produced anything on the mutability of species beyond that inadequate exposition bequeathed to Emma's care. Then there was the annoying Edward Bulwer-Lytton, who had put into one of his novels a character called Professor Long, who had written two huge volumes on limpets. There could not be much doubt as to who he had in mind; and, when you become a standing joke, it is time to do something about it. And then —frightening thought!—it was always possible that someone might forestall him.

8

Procrastination

CHARLES, AMONG other things, became a pigeon fancier—his fellow fanciers with semifamiliarity addressed him as "Squire." He corresponded voluminously with breeders of all sorts and read indefatigibly in horticultural and agricultural journals. For he was interested in the mutation, or change, of species that man creates by artificial, or what might be called *un*natural, selection. He carried out slow experiments with seeds in salt water. For he was concerned with the significance of the geographical distribution of life, both animal and vegetable, and in the means by which this was effected. Could seeds, for instance, travel in ocean currents and still germinate after long immersion, should they by chance reach another land?

Always, he condemned his grandfather and Lamarck for

their wild generalizations and unsubstantiated speculations; nevertheless, how he loved speculation and generalization. "How delightful," he once confided, "to have many points fermenting in one's brain!" The difference was that, with him, there would never be any peace of mind until speculations were tested to the limit. Speculation and observation were twin necessities, both essential and one sterile without the other: "It is a fatal fault to reason while observing, though so necessary beforehand and so useful afterwards." So, he went on collecting his facts, and reasoning about them, before and after.

He had been led to one basic idea by the essay of the economist Malthus, to which we have already referred. Malthus talked of the pressure of human population upon subsistence—in plainer words, upon the food that kept them alive. Human beings had the power of multiplying themselves in twenty-five years, but nature could not support such a population; some, therefore, did not survive. The same thing, Darwin realized, was happening in the rest of the living world, a continual "struggle for existence." Add to this the idea that species of animals and plants were not immutable but varied, and one reached the conclusion that, to quote his autobiography, "favourable variations would tend to be preserved, and unfavourable ones to be destroyed. The result of this would be the formation of new species."

But these variations that nature worked upon and sifted out by "natural selection," killing off the unsuccessful and encouraging those more fit—how exactly and why exactly did they come about? Suddenly, the answer, or at least part of it, came to him: "I can remember the very spot in the road, whilst in my carriage, when to my joy the solution occurred to me."

Still, however, Darwin hesitated to publish. The year 1856 arrived, and that naturalist and explorer of the Amazon Alfred Russel Wallace again swam into Darwin's horizon, a little more definitely. Wallace published, in a magazine of natural history, an article "On the Law Which Has Regulated the Introduction of New Species." Charles Lyell read it, saw that Wallace was also thinking in terms of "natural selection," and at once urged his friend at least to publish a sketch of his ideas, lest he be entirely forestalled.

Darwin's reply was that he hated the idea of writing merely to establish priority, admitting at the same time, however, that, being human, he would be "vexed if any one were to publish my doctrine before me." His other great friend and supporter, Joseph Hooker, was brought in for consultation; and Charles, protesting that he was not ready and that it was "dreadfully unphilosophic" to publish without full supporting details, agreed reluctantly to spend a couple of months in producing "a *very thin* and little volume."

He began. But, soon, he was back to his salt-water tanks and his experiments and was talking of publishing "perhaps in a year's time." The next year, he wrote to Wallace, saying that their lines of thought were similar, that he could not explain his ideas on variation in species in a letter, but that he was writing a book about it that might go to press perhaps "in two years' time." Nothing whatever was said in this letter to indicate that he also had ideas on natural selection. Darwin did write, however, about this time, to his friend the American naturalist Asa Gray, setting out his whole theory of evolution. Meanwhile, his book, no longer in the least "thin," progressed steadily but slowly.

Then came the blow. In June, 1858, there dropped through the letter box at Down House as startling and important a communication as had dropped into his father's letter box at Shrewsbury twenty-seven years before. This was not an invitation to a great opportunity; it was an intimation that he had almost certainly missed one. Enclosed was an essay by Wallace entitled *On the Tendency of Varieties To Depart Indefinitely from the Original Type,* and with it a polite and friendly covering note from the author expressing the hope that its idea would be as "new" to Darwin as it was to himself and would be considered to "supply the missing factor to explain the origin of species." Wallace asked that Darwin, if he thought it worthy, send it on to Lyell.

Charles did send it on to Lyell. It was, he suggested, in a highly restrained understatement, "well worth reading." But then he added his true thoughts: *"Your words have come true with a vengeance—that I should be forestalled. I never saw a more striking coincidence; if Wallace had my MS. sketch written out in 1842 he could not have made a better short abstract! Even his terms now stand as heads of my chapters."*

Darwin was terribly perturbed, as well he might be. It was true that his own claim to priority—with his half-written book, with his sketch of 1842, his letter to Asa Gray—was absolutely cast-iron and that there was nothing in Wallace's essay that these writings of his did not cover, and more fully. It was true that Wallace, although he had independently arrived at the same theory, had owed a good deal to Darwin's earlier writings, particularly the descriptions and hints contained in his journal of the voyage of the *Beagle.* But it was equally true that Darwin had published nothing and that Lyell now had in his hands an essay by someone else that completely set out Darwin's own ideas and which that someone innocently expected, if it was "worthy," that Lyell should proclaim to the world. Darwin genuinely hated any idea of competing for fame and publicity. But, after all, he was human. "So all my originality," he wrote miserably to Lyell, "will be smashed." Yet, obviously, he must do the honorable thing. He half wrote a letter to Wallace, offering to suppress his own work entirely, and then destroyed it. He sought advice also from Hooker. He hoped desperately that his two friends would find a way out both honorable and satisfactory to himself.

In fact, they did. Hooker, the younger man, acted with speed and decision. He sent for Charles's sketch of 1842 and his letter to Asa Gray, and had his wife make a résumé of the two. Then he and Lyell faced a meeting of the Linnean Society, London's premier biological society, whose members had assembled to hear a paper on the fixity of species by one George Bentham, nephew of the philosopher Jeremy Bentham. The two staunch supporters of Darwin made short speeches merely asserting the importance of the occasion and then sat back while the secretary read something very different from what they had been summoned to hear—the two papers, in twin harness, as it were, that of Alfred Russel Wallace and Mrs. Hooker's résumé of Darwin's work.

That was on July 1, 1858. The members, duly impressed, rose to no facile clamor of denial of the unorthodox principles announced. They merely murmured and talked among themselves, it is reported. Then they went their several ways; and the papers, as is the fate of all papers read before learned societies, found themselves buried in due course within the severe covers of the society's journal.

Nevertheless, the cat had been let out of the bag, and, as cats go, it was a pretty fierce, lively, and vocal one.

9

The Origin of Species

THERE COULD be no more dilatoriness now, no more holding back for just one more month or so, one more year or so, while yet more convincing evidence was collected. Darwin, who, characteristically, had kept away from the Linnean Society meeting at which the twin papers were read, now set about with some enthusiasm to produce a résumé of his half-written book for appearance in the society's journal. He somehow felt released now; the die was cast and all his scruples and hesitations could be set aside and forgotten. He wrote rapidly and with enjoyment. Inevitably, the résumé grew to book size again. But John Murray, the publisher of the revised and popular edition of the *Beagle* journal, was willing and anxious to publish this book too.

With only occasional delaying bouts of ill health, Charles worked hard. Proofs began to come in for correction, and Charles, in the way of great men with ideas to express, gave his publisher qualms and headaches with the enormous amount of corrections that he made. He also gave him qualms and headaches with what was going to appear in the book. Murray found the central theory not only startling, but "as absurd as though one should contemplate a fruitful union between a poker and a rabbit." Could not Darwin perhaps start again, with a book that merely set out his revolutionary views quite briefly and gave most of its space to a dissertation on the author's observations and experiences in breeding pigeons—"everybody is interested in pigeons"? Darwin refused, and Murray withdrew his idiotic proposal. Then the title was objected to. Was not the phrase "natural selection" too unfamiliar to the ordinary reader? Again Charles overruled the objection. Then Lyell put his oar in— it was Darwin's friends who were being cautious now, not Darwin. Would it not be better for the book to acknowledge that there had been a divine and separate creation at least of man himself? Again Darwin refused: "I would give absolutely nothing for the theory of Natural Selection, if it requires miraculous additions at any one stage of descent."

At length, when Darwin was thoroughly sick of the whole thing, and again a sick man himself, the book appeared. The date was November 24, 1859, and the title, in full, was *On the Origin of Species by Means of Natural Selection, or the Preservation of Favoured Races in the Struggle for Life*. Its whole edition of 1,250 copies was sold out at once, and a second edition was in demand.

What had Charles Darwin done, what was the gist of the

Charles Darwin in 1860, at the age of fifty-one.

book, this his great Theory of Evolution? Let us try to put the answer down as succinctly as possible.

✓(1) Life of all kinds and at all times has shown a tremendous variety, and a variety in which one kind of plant or creature may show differences from another kind by a whole series of minute steps.

/ (2) Varieties of life fit themselves to their particular environment with great exactness.

/ (3) These facts lead one to suppose not a vast multitude of separate acts of creation, but a process of gradual change, or evolution.

/ (4) How this evolution could have come about can be seen if we consider two phenomena of nature. (a) *The struggle for existence:* In all forms of life too many offspring are produced and only some will survive. (b) *The mutability of species:* Variations occur in all forms of life and are inherited; offspring are not all the same or exactly the same as their parents.

/ (5) These two phenomena will act together in a sifting process that may be called "natural selection"; only those varieties that are the better fitted to their environment will thus survive.

/ (6) This process, over a long period of time, is sufficient to account for the gradual change in the forms of life and the appearance of new species, in fact, for *organic evolution.*

It was in the explanation of this last link in the chain of reasoning (Number 6) that Darwin had had his moment of sudden inspiration and understanding. In the words of his autobiography, it was not clear to him why, given that creatures could change or modify from generation to generation, they should, in fact, do so to such an extent that they diverged into separate species. "The solution, as I believe, is that the modified offspring of all dominant and increasing forms tend to become adapted to many and diversified places in the economy of nature."

Let us help toward our own understanding by taking an example from what must have happened when the giant reptiles were disappearing from the earth. Those of the probably little rat-like type of mammal—and this mammalian type must certainly have been a "dominant and increasing form," an adventurous creature—who elected to climb up into the trees and to live there would find a very different environment facing them. Now, those of the generations of new offspring that had better sight than smell and that had paws better for branch-clinging than for ground-scratching would tend to survive. Gradually, in small degrees, the animal in the new environment would change, so that, were it to return to its old habitat, it would not even recognize those decendants of its long-past forefathers who had stayed put as being the same animal at all. In fact, a new species, or even a new genus, would have evolved. The same thing could happen if some members of a species should spread and find themselves cut off by changes in the earth's crust, the growth of an intervening forest, for instance, the rise of a mountain range, or the incursion of the sea.

Now, let us return to the book itself, *The Origin of Species*, and to its author. It must be realized how much of an ideological bombshell this new theory of evolution was. It was not only that it set the literal interpretation of the Bible at nought and sought to destroy, for good, the ancient belief that life had come about by a series of separate creations. For some time, the educated world, at least, had been familiar with such new ideas, although it had been reluctant to accept them. But here was something more. Not only was creation set aside, but any God-given purpose was set aside as well. Darwin's "Great Cause" behind life was no more than a purely material and mechanical one, as well as a harsh and unpleasant one: the survival of the fittest by means of natural selection—by means, that is to say, of a Nature extremely "red" (as Alfred, Lord Tennyson had called it ten years earlier) "in tooth and claw."

Darwin himself realized the implications clearly enough. That was obviously one of the reasons that he had been so reluctant to publish and had been subconsciously anxious to seize on any excuse for not doing so. It caused him, too, to await the reception of the book with very considerable trepidation. Were there things in it that dear old Henslow, for instance, could never swallow—would he be so shocked that a most precious friendship of years would be broken? What would Sedgwick, who had reported to his old school that he was doing "admirable work," say now? Would that die-hard but brilliant anatomist and naturalist Richard Owen explode? There would be no friendship lost there—nobody seemed to like the man—but he was important and influential.

Darwin sent out advance copies to his friends and to all the important naturalists, enclosing notes that revealed his anxiety and also, sometimes, his innate humbleness of spirit. To Henslow he wrote, "I fear, however, that you will not approve of your pupil in this case." To John Lubbock, later to become a great prehistorian and the first Lord Avebury: "No doubt I am in part in error, perhaps wholly so, though I cannot see the blindness of my ways." To Alfred Russel Wallace: "I do not think your share in the theory will be overlooked by the real judges." To a friend whom he had no hope of converting, "Lord, how savage you will be, if you read it!" To Thomas Huxley (of whom more later), less humbly and more combatively: "I am very far from expecting to convert you to many of my heresies; but if, on the whole, you and two or three others think I am on the right road, I shall not care what the mob of naturalists think." The others whose opinion he most cared about were, of course, Lyell and Hooker; if Lyell, Hooker, and Huxley agreed with him, then his theory was "safe."

So, Charles Darwin sent his child, his lifework, out into the world and waited for the reaction, no doubt going over often in his mind the main argument of his book and the more controversial things that he had written.

The book, after a historical sketch of opinion to date and an Introduction that opens with the disarmingly reasonable remark, "When on board H.M.S. *Beagle* as naturalist, I was much struck with certain facts," begins with a dissertation of "Variations Under Domestication"—in other words, under man-made, or unnatural, selection. It was obvious, indeed spectacular, what differences could be made in the forms of animal and plant life by *that* sort of sifting, that sort of use of the fact of "mutation" between one generation and the next—look at the fancier's pigeons, for instance.

Next, by a natural transition, came "Variations Under Nature"; then, a chapter headed "Struggle for Existence"; and a following one called "Natural Selection; or the Survival of the Fittest."*

The rest was elaboration, argument, and the considering of difficulties. First, what were the laws governing variation between one generation and the next? He had to admit that here there was little more at present than a vast ignorance, although the fact itself was plain enough. Of the difficulties that he tackled, an important one was the inadequacy of the geological record, the vast gaps that were in it. He knew

* This phraseology was not used in the first edition of the book, however (see p. 91, below).

that, for most of his readers, to have pointed out the great similarity of many extinct fossil animals to living forms would not be enough; they would want a neat and complete series, throughout time, showing a gradual evolution to the modern form—such a series as can now, in fact, be given—from eohippus to the present-day horse. He gave the answer that is still given today, although now with more certainty: "I have attempted to show that the geological record is extremely imperfect; that only a small portion of the globe has been geologically explored with care; that only certain classes of organic beings have been largely preserved in a fossil state; that the number both of specimens and of species, preserved in our museums, is absolutely as nothing compared with the incalculable number of generations which must have passed away even during a single [geological] formation," the chances of any particular animal's bones becoming fossilized being infinitesimal.

Finally, he turned from defense to attack, skillfully marshaling an overwhelming mass of supporting evidence, which was what made Darwin's book so different from, and so much greater than, his grandfather's—so much greater, for that matter, than Wallace's slender essay. He showed how the geological record, the story of the rocks, made nonsense of the old creationist idea, imperfect though that record might be. He elaborated the significance of the present geographical distribution of differing forms of plants and animals, on isolated islands (Galápagos) for instance. He gave a chapter to the evidence of physical make-up, the pattern of living creatures. "What can be more curious," he asked, "than that the hand of a man, formed for grasping, that of a mole for digging, the leg of the horse, the paddle of the porpoise, and the wing of the bat, should all be con-

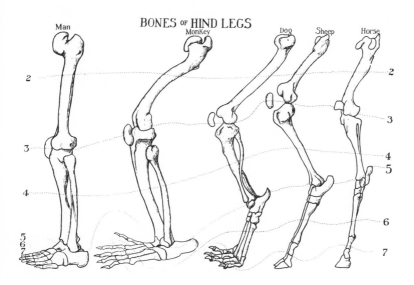

BONES OF HIND LEGS

Man   MonKey   Dog   Sheep   Horse

Bones of hind legs. The similarity in pattern and position of the bones was valid evidence for the theory of evolution.

structed on the same pattern, and should include similar bones, in the same relative positions? How curious it is, to give a subordinate though striking instance, that the hind-feet of the kangaroo, which are so well fitted for bounding over the open plains,—those of the climbing, leaf-eating koala, equally well fitted for grasping the branches of trees, —those of the ground-dwelling insect or root-eating bandi-coots,—and those of some other Australian marsupials,— should all be constructed on the same extraordinary type, namely with the bones of the second and third digits ex-tremely slender and enveloped within the same skin, so that they appear like a single toe furnished with two claws."

It was, of course, not only curious but significant, and pointed only one way, that all these creatures were the

progeny of a single ancient—millions of years ancient—
ancestral type. In such a way did Darwin give not only the
more obvious example, but also the little-known example
from out of the ordered storehouse of that remarkable mem-
ory of his, enriched, as it was, by initial travel and sub-
sequent voluminous reading. In the same way, he dealt with
vestigial organs (see Glossary)—why did that mammal, the
whale, possess the utterly useless rudiments of an embryonic
back leg?—and with embryology, the science of the early
development or prenatal babyhood of individual lives, point-
ing out the curious fact "that various parts in the same individual which are exactly alike during an early embryonic
period, become widely different and serve for widely different purposes in the adult state." And, by way of proof, he
quoted a statement by the Estonian naturalist Karl E. von
Baer, that he had in his possession "two little embryos in
spirit, whose names I have omitted to attach, and at present
I am quite unable to say to what class they belong. They
may be lizards or small birds, or very young mammalia, so
complete is the similarity in the mode of formation of the
head and trunk in these animals."

At length, after 350 pages or so—more in some editions—
Darwin comes to his recapitulation and conclusion. Here he
takes the bit firmly between his teeth and all diffidence
makes way for a soaring confidence and optimism. He cen-
sures the out-of-date creationists: "These authors seem no
more startled at a miraculous act of creation than at an ordinary birth. But do they really believe that at innumerable
periods in the earth's history certain elemental atoms have
been commanded suddenly to flash into living tissues? Do
they believe that at each supposed act of creation one individual or many were produced? Were all the infinitely

numerous kinds of animals and plants created as eggs or seed, or as full grown? And in the case of mammals, were they created bearing the false marks of nourishment from the mother's womb?" He even ventures to suppose that "all animals and plants are descended from some one prototype," and—more significant still—feels sure that "much light will be thrown on the origin of man and his history." He dares to foresee, from the acceptance of his thesis, a great freeing from vain shackles, an opening up of hitherto untrodden fields of inquiry. Finally, surveying with no qualms but with unbounded optimism his "natural selection" and his "survival of the fittest," he declares, to end his book:

> Thus, from the war of nature, from famine and death, the most exalted object which we are capable of conceiving, namely, the production of the higher animals, directly follows. There is grandeur in this view of life, with its several powers, having been originally breathed by the Creator into a few forms or into one; and that, whilst this planet has gone cycling on according to the fixed law of gravity, from so simple a beginning endless forms most beautiful and most wonderful have been, and are being evolved.

10

Reception of a Book

Professor Sedgwick, the old and respected geologist, wrote to say that he had really had to laugh at some of the things in *The Origin of Species*. His was, however, not a rude letter; but, rather, a very pained one. Other things, he said, he had read with absolute sorrow, "because I think them utterly false and grievously mischievous."

Many of the letters from the recipients of advance copies were, however, cheering to the anxious author. Charles Kingsley, the fiery and reforming clergyman who wrote (among other things) *The Water Babies* and *Westward Ho!*, backed up Darwin's claim that there was no reason why the book should shock religious feelings. Henslow went "a little way" with Darwin and assured his old pupil that he was not shocked. Lubbock went all the way, as did Hooker and Hux-

ley; Lyell went nearly all the way, boggling only at the in-
clusion of man in the evolutionary scheme. Darwin was immensely relieved. He wrote to Lyell, whose books had done
so much for him as a young man, but who, nevertheless, had
always stuck to being a "creationist": "I honour you most
sincerely. To have maintained, in the position of a master, one
side of a question for thirty years, and then deliberately give
it up, is a fact to which I much doubt whether the records of
science offer a parallel." He now had, he felt, what we might
call his three just men to agree with him, and his theory was
indeed "safe." Thomas Huxley warned him, however, that
whether safe or not, his theory was certainly going to arouse
opposition. He hoped that Darwin would not allow himself
"to be in any way disgusted or annoyed by the considerable
abuse and misrepresentation which, unless I greatly mistake,
is in store for you." He was, he added with enthusiasm,
"sharpening his beak and claws" in readiness to enter the
fray on Darwin's behalf.

Then the reviews began to come in. The serious and respected *Athenaeum*, under the appearance of fairness, was
slightly derisive and more than a little unkind. The author
(Darwin) showed himself, it observed archly, "supremely
loving of his own offspring" (i.e., the book) and undoubtedly "selected" it to be "the successful competitor in the
struggle for existence." It also started the legend that the
book claimed that "man descends from the monkeys"—something that Darwin never said. The *Saturday Review* and the
Daily News were more or less against him, the latter accusing him of merely plagiarizing a little-known earlier book by
an anonymous author called *Vestiges of Creation*.

And then came *The Times* review. It was over three columns long, and was a sympathetic and brilliantly clear ex-

position of the book, ending with a declaration that its doctrine was superior to any yet propounded and should be accepted with no more than "an active doubt," the further scientific investigations of the next twenty years being sure to test its findings in detail. It was a review more likely to recommend the book to thoughtful readers than any out-and-out partisan defense. Darwin was delighted and suspected that Huxley was the reviewer. He was right.

But then came some more hard knocks. Sedgwick wrote an indignant, and unsigned, notice in the *Spectator*, which Darwin thought "savage and unfair." Those big guns of the nineteenth-century critical world, the *Edinburgh* and the *Quarterly* reviews, each had long articles on Darwin's book. The first of these was also unsigned, and Darwin thought it "extremely malignant," but clever. He had reason to believe that it was written by Richard Owen.

The *Quarterly* article was by a bishop—Samuel Wilberforce, then Bishop of Oxford, son of a really greater man, the William Wilberforce who did so much to put down Negro slavery. He was a persuasive upholder of orthodoxy and had earned the title, among the disrespectful, of "Soapy Sam." The bishop's review was kind enough not to doubt Darwin's Christianity, but warned him patronizingly to restrain his "exuberant fancy."

Darwin was probably fortunate, in the long run, to have had as his most active opponents no one more dangerous than Richard Owen and Samuel Wilberforce; he certainly was lucky to have such a friend and champion as Thomas Huxley, the man who came to be known as "Darwin's bulldog."

Huxley was sixteen years younger than Darwin, and so was thirty-five years old in 1860. He also had had his learning enlarged and his enthusiasm fired by a voyage in a naval surveying ship, on which he had been the assistant surgeon, although his interest was natural history. Now, he was a brilliant and popular lecturer in that subject at the School of Mines, later to become London's Imperial College. He had already crossed swords with Owen, over a certain matter of interpretation of the significance of the bones of the human skull—not to put too fine a point on it. Owen had been accused of talking nonsense, and Huxley had had cause to dislike him. And then had come Darwin's notorious book. For Huxley, it had seemed to be just what he had been waiting for; it appealed to him absolutely.

The stage was now set, therefore, for a sort of climax to the controversy that Darwin's book had set going. *The Origin of Species* had reached the general reading public, and rumors of it had reached beyond them. People came to the British Museum in numbers, it was reported with surprise, asking to see evidence of "species." And the controversy, despite the kind letters and the modicum of favorable reviews that Charles had received, showed most definitely a bias *against* the presumptuous and disturbing naturalist. Thomas Huxley was later to talk of "a gale of popular prejudice" and an "outburst of antagonism."

The scene for the climax was Oxford, where Samuel Wilberforce resided as bishop and where, in the summer of 1860, the British Association was holding its annual meeting of public lectures and discussions. The bishop was in attendance, as were Owen, Hooker, and Huxley. The author of the ensuing controversy was somewhere else, taking a health cure. If ever someone needed a champion, Charles Darwin was the man.

The first day of the Association's meeting, Wednesday, June 27, was quiet and ordinary enough. No mention was

made of *The Origin of Species*, though everybody was thinking about it and expecting excitement. On Thursday, an
amiable Oxford professor of botany read to the zoology section a paper on "The Final Causes of the Sexuality of Plants,
with Particular Reference to Mr. Darwin's Work on *The
Origin of Species*. Huxley was there, Owen was there; Henslow, now an old man, was in the chair.

After the lecture—which was pro-Darwin—Huxley was
invited to speak. But Huxley apparently suspected that
this would be an emotional occasion and demurred at discussing the vexed and important question before "a general
audience, in which sentiment would unduly interfere with
intellect." Richard Owen had no such scruples—observing,
however, that he "wished to approach the subject in the
spirit of the philosopher." There were facts, he continued,
that the public ought to know. The brain of the gorilla, he
asserted roundly, "presented more differences, as compared
with the brain of man, than it did when compared with the
brains of the very lowest and most problematical of the
Quadrumana" (see Glossary). Huxley rose at once and flatly
contradicted him. This, he admitted, was an unusual proce-
dure, which he would justify elsewhere. It was more than
unusual; it was bold and dramatic—Owen was "Sir Richard," greatly senior in years to Huxley, and the leading
anatomist of his time.

Friday was quiet, at least at the meetings. Outside, excited gossip and rumor were being delightedly exchanged.
Owen was reported to be plotting a counterattack on the
morrow and to be priming Bishop Wilberforce with a good
explosive charge for when he was to speak after another
lecture that had Mr. Darwin's name in its title. As for the

bishop, he was reported to be rustling up his clerical supporters—after all, the meetings were open to the public.

The day and the hour came. Sir Richard Owen thought it circumspect not to be present. Huxley, still disliking the idea of emotional, rather than scientific, reaction, had not intended to be present either; nor had Hooker. Both were enticed inside by friends, Huxley even being accused of contemplating desertion. "Oh, if you are going to take it that way!" Huxley answered, and went in with the rest.

The meeting was to have been in a lecture room of the New University Library. It soon became clear that the room would not be big enough, and a move was made, to the library proper. Even that was hardly big enough. The bishop's clergy made a solid, dark phalanx in the middle, while their wives, less somberly dressed and ready to flutter their handkerchiefs at the slightest provocation, sat by the windows. Undergraduates, anxious to see the fun, if any, filled the spaces in-between.

The paper to be read was on the somewhat unlikely subject of "The Intellectual Development of Europe, Considered with Reference to the Views of Mr. Darwin and Others," the author a certain Dr. Draper of New York. Henslow was again in the chair, and Huxley and Hooker were both on the platform. The bishop arrived late, pushing his way through the crowd. The atmosphere was tense—so tense, indeed, that people gave conflicting accounts of what happened.

Dr. Draper (it seems) did his best to soothe the excited crowd, and, in fact, nearly put them to sleep. They politely bore with him for an hour—was this going to be a dull meeting after all? But not so; the crowd, and especially the undergraduates, were losing their patience. The next three speakers, in turn, were shouted down. The third, a man with a strange accent, sought curiously, and rashly, to illustrate the point of Darwin's thesis that all were interested in by a diagram on the blackboard. "Let this point A be the man," he announced, "and let that point B be the mawnkey."

"Mawnkey, mawnkey!" chanted the delighted undergraduates, and the third speaker sat down. This was certainly becoming an unusual meeting. The bishop rose.

A somewhat biased hearer afterward reported that Bishop Samuel Wilberforce "spouted for half an hour with inimitable spirit, ugliness and emptiness and unfairness." But "Soapy Sam" was a good rhetorician, nevertheless, and knew how to sway a crowd. This was the sort of thing that Huxley had been afraid of. The bishop was at first jovially amusing, then brutally scoffing. He ridiculed Darwin's "proofs," and denounced his conclusions as "an hypothesis, raised most unphilosophically to the dignity of a causal theory." Hooker and Huxley thought that they recognized another hand— Owen's—behind that grand but vague scientific remark.

But then the bishop's exuberance led to his own undoing. Not content with other people's phrases, if that is what they were, he descended from science to the cheapest and silliest of scoring-points. Reaching his peroration, he turned to Huxley with a sarcastic smile and asked him whether it was "through your grandfather or your grandmother that you claim your descent from a monkey?"

Huxley excitedly struck his hand on his knee. "The Lord hath delivered him into mine hands," he murmured.

The bishop sat down to a roar of applause and a fluttering of feminine handkerchiefs. A cry rose up for Huxley to reply. When silence was regained, Henslow called on him to speak.

Huxley rose, pale and impressive with his long frock coat and high wing collar, his pale actor's face beneath leonine black hair, and his long, thin, expressive mouth.

He achieved his effect by a contrasted quietness. He appealed to reason, not prejudice. He defended Darwin's theory, not merely as a hypothesis, but as the "best explanation of the development of species yet put forward." Then he became even more quiet and grave. He would not, he said, be ashamed to have a monkey for an ancestor. But, turning to the uncertainly smiling bishop, he would be ashamed indeed if it were a man "who prostituted the gifts of culture and of eloquence to the service of prejudice and falsehood." There was instant commotion. One lady achieved fame by fainting.

Then, when order was restored, there was one last dramatic moment, more dramatic perhaps to us who read of it than to those who witnessed it. Many may not have recognized the elderly but handsome man with aristocratic features who rose, held a Bible aloft, and, declaring his belief in its unimpeachable authority, denied the claim that *The Origin of Species* was a logical statement of fact, and stated how much he regretted its publication. The speaker was Admiral Robert FitzRoy, once captain of H.M.S. *Beagle*.

Hooker finally wound up with a further defense of the controversial book, accusing Wilberforce of obviously never having read it.

That night the meeting was the talk of the Association. And, as for Charles Darwin, he was heartily glad that he had not been there.

II

Two Vital Questions

It was the power of *The Origin of Species,* besides its reasonableness, that won acceptance, the feeling the reader was given that the author from his years of thought, fact-collecting, and experimenting had behind his many quoted examples an overwhelming weight of further, unused evidence. Alfred Russel Wallace, whose firm friend Darwin remained, wrote generously: "As to the theory of Natural Selection itself, I shall always maintain it to be actually yours and yours only. You had worked it out in details I had never thought of, years before I had a ray of light on the subject, and my paper would never have convinced anybody or been noticed as more than an ingenious speculation, whereas your book has revolutionized the study of natural history, and carried away captive the best men of the present age."

Professor Huxley, with his boldness, his quick wit, and his brilliant pen, lectured and wrote in an all-out effort to explain and popularize Darwin's theory. Darwin was delighted. Herbert Spencer, philosopher, sociologist, and psychologist, and an evolutionist and almost a Darwinian before Darwin, wrote learnedly and philosophically on the subject, and Darwin was a little bewildered, as well as grateful, although he did borrow from Spencer the phrase "survival of the fittest." The only supporter who, surprisingly, let him down was the admired Charles Lyell, who, in his book *The Antiquity of Man*, appearing three years after *The Origin of Species*, could not bring himself to be more definite than to say, "If it should ever be rendered highly probable that species change by variation and natural selection . . ." *If*, forsooth! Lyell was sitting on the fence, after all. However, the book was helping the public to get used to the idea that man was not necessarily a unique and recent creation and might have ancestors at least rather different from himself—the Neanderthal skull was, for instance, being closely studied. Lyell wrote, rather pathetically, to Darwin saying, "I have been forced to give up my old faith without thoroughly seeing my way to a new one." The two men remained good friends.

All in all, the battle for acceptance was slowly but steadily being won. In 1872, by which time four French, five German, three American, three Russian, and at least one each of Dutch, Italian, and Swedish editions of *The Origin of Species* had appeared, the sixth and last English edition came out, and Darwin was able to write in it: "As a record of a former state of things, I have retained in the foregoing paragraphs, and elsewhere, several sentences which imply that naturalists believe in the separate creation of each species;

and I have been much censured for having thus expressed myself. But undoubtedly this was the general belief when the first edition of the present work appeared. . . . Now things are wholly changed, and almost every naturalist admits the great principle of evolution."

That was 1872, and Charles was sixty-three years old and had ten more years to live. What had he himself been doing in the twelve years since the publication of his greatest book?

For one thing, he had written and had published four more books, entitled *On the Various Contrivances by Which Orchids Are Fertilized by Insects; The Movements and Habits of Climbing Plants; The Variation of Animals and Plants Under Domestication;* and *The Descent of Man, and Selection in Relation to Sex.*

They certainly comprise a large number of words—short and snappy titles were by no means the fashion in those days—and, probably out of all of them, the one that strikes the eye will be *The Descent of Man.*

If so, our eyes will not have been mistaken. *The Descent of Man* is Darwin's most important book after *The Origin of Species.* The curious things about it are, firstly, that he did not want to write it, and even tried to pass the job on to somebody else; and, secondly, that its thunder was really already stolen before it was written.

What Darwin had intended to do was to set out in great detail his whole theory. After all, this had been what he had been engaged on when Alfred Russel Wallace's untimely essay had shocked him into what he considered most precipitate action. *The Origin of Species* was really only a sketch, a résumé; now, he thought, he would get down to the real thing and produce three large volumes.

Perhaps fortunately, he was never able to fulfill this ambition—perhaps it was unfulfillable—and he had to do with a second best. He turned to the subject that he knew was both the most fundamental and the most shrouded in ignorance, not least his own. This was "variations," *how* one generation of an animal or plant managed to be different from those that preceded it. There were variations under the hand of the human breeder and fancier, and there were variations under nature—the latter had never been properly tackled. Both, however, must surely be subject to the same inherent laws.

Darwin struggled with this subject for eight years, the two books, about orchids and climbing plants respectively, being, as it were, thrown off in the way of light—comparatively light—relief.

He found the problem of the mechanics of heredity intractable. As a matter of fact, although Darwin was entirely unaware of it, a certain Austrian friar, the Abbé Gregor Mendel, was at this very time experimenting elaborately with sweet peas in his monastery garden at Brünn and propounding a theory that the world was later to accept. But, before it was accepted, Mendel had to die with his work unrecognized, and his obscurely published papers had to be subsequently revived and recognized by others; the scientific world of the nineteenth century knew no more of Mendelism than did its greatest and most well-known naturalist, and that naturalist had to struggle on on his own. And, for once, Darwin failed to see objectively enough, and preconceived ideas prevented him from reaching the truth; *The Variation of Animals and Plants* is really Darwin's one great failure. He recognized, as Mendel did, that the offspring of two varieties of plant or animal, a hybrid, did not have its parents' characteristics blended in a sort of amorphous blancmange, but inherited them distinctly in certain and varying proportions; he realized that these inherited characteristics could be either "prepotent" or the reverse (Mendel's *dominant* and *recessive*). But his final theory was a sort of Mendelism standing on its head; heredity not hidden in the chromosomes of the gonads, or the male and female sexual cells, and from there issuing outward into all the cells of the new life; but, on the contrary, hidden, in the form of minute corpuscles, in every cell of the parents and carried by the blood and lymph streams to the gametes, or sex cells.

These corpuscles Darwin christened "gemmules," and his theory incorporating them he called "pangenesis," or, as one might translate the Greek, "beginnings everywhere." He produced his theory tentatively, as quite unprovable but the best yet evolved to fit the facts. He hoped people would like it—and wondered whether they would.

In fact, they did not like it much, but were good enough to agree that its author's claim that it was the best so far could not be denied—which, indeed, it could not. Darwin had to be content with that, and turned to other things.

For awhile he turned to relaxation. Like all good middle-class Victorians, he went on seaside holidays with his large family, five boys and two girls, all now in their teens or twenties, but none of them yet married. Charles Darwin was famous now, however, and holidays could not be entirely ordinary. On the Isle of Wight they met Tennyson and Longfellow, the first seeming rather "absurd" to Charles and Emma and the latter talking interestingly about spiritualism and American naturalists. Charles spent much of the holiday jogging through the country lanes on his pony Tommy, brought down specially for the purpose.

The next year they all went to Barmouth. But Darwin, in the meantime, had had a fall from his pony, and was sad to find himself sick, feeble, and shaky, a bearded old man who could not even contemplate the sort of energetic geologizing expeditions, bounding over the rocks and cliffs, that he had indulged in here in his youth. Then they went across into Shropshire and visited his old home in Shrewsbury, now in the hands of another. The new owner was so impressed by the eminence of his visitor that he would not let him alone, and Darwin was disappointed—he would have liked five quiet minutes in the conservatory, to be able to conjure up a vision of his old father.

Fame also meant more entertaining at home, and Charles and Emma were better at this now than they had been in the first years of their marriage. Indeed, a visit to the Darwins at Down House must have been rather a delightful experience, for the great man had lost none of his kindliness nor taken on any pomposity in the least. In the evening, there he would be, his lanky form stretched out on the sofa, a shawl perhaps over his shoulders, talking easily, though in the somewhat long and involved sentences he used—his quick brain and his fair-mindedness thinking of all sorts of qualifications to his sentences before he had gotten halfway through them. Sometimes he would catch himself doing this, and laugh. He was good, too, at drawing out his visitors on their favorite subjects, for he liked to listen and learn.

Wallace came to stay with him, as did many eminent visiting Americans; Samuel Butler, who had just written his *Erewhon*; Sullivan, one-time lieutenant on the *Beagle*, who had since done missionary work among the Fuegians and was now a K.C.B. (Knight Commander of the Bath); and the formidable and irascible Thomas Carlyle. Carlyle must have unbent, or been unbent, considerably, for he admitted afterward that it was "a good while since I have seen any brother mortal that had more of true sociability and human attraction for me."

But, by his nature, Darwin could not cease either to work or to think—"When I am obliged to give up observation and experiment," he said, "I shall die." After the unsatisfactoriness and somewhat cool reception of *The Variation of Animals and Plants* and its "pangenesis," he turned to a new and important book, in which he planned to cover the descent of man, sexual selection, and the expressions of the emotions in man and animals. As usual, he wrote more lengthily than he had planned to, and the last subject was dropped, to appear later separately. Even so, the book, when it came out, was really two books in one, the long and very detailed account of animal courtship, sexual characteristics, and their effect upon "the survival of the fittest" having only a slender connection with the arguments concerning the evolution of man.

As we have said, Darwin did not want to write a book on the evolution of man. He even offered all his notes and material to Wallace, who declined—rather, perhaps, as anyone might who was offered a "Do It Yourself" kit for a time bomb. Was Darwin a coward, then? One has only to look at the absolute honesty and forthrightness of his publications, in which he never made any concession to expediency, to answer that question. Undoubtedly, however, he did hate controversy and the hurting of other people's religious feelings. The public had already singled out as the factor of prime importance in his theory the idea that man himself was no more than part of an animal world and of the evolutionary process; and, since they had become so emotionally worked up about it, it would be better, he thought, if someone else wrote the book that was to deal specifically with that question. Certainly the book needed to be written. And no one else would do it? Very well then! His health was better and he wrote quickly. The book appeared in 1871.

How far, Darwin was asking, were the general conclusions arrived at in *The Origin of Species* applicable to man? That was the question; and he proceeded to examine and answer it with his usual thoroughness in this, his second most important book.

He was far from being dogmatic, but now, with a lifetime of thought and experience behind him, he was more certain of himself—he could even indulge in a little wry humor. Having admitted that many of his views were highly speculative, he remarked: "False facts are highly injurious to the progress of science, for they often endure long; but false views, if supported by some evidence, do little harm, for every one takes a salutary pleasure in proving their falseness: and when this is done, one path towards error is closed and the road to truth is often at the same time opened." Here, incidentally, was a very wise statement, as well as a slightly rueful one.

Much of what Darwin wrote in this book may seem to us now to be stating the obvious. But he had not only to prove his point against opposition, but also to correct a misapprehension. The misapprehension was based on a popular misunderstanding and oversimplification of his views that had rapidly grown up and is, in fact, even today often still with us. The present writer remembers falling into casual conversation with a man on a park seat. Somehow the subject of Darwin came up. "Ah," cried the man, "the chap who said we are all descended from monkeys!"—and added, for good measure: "No wonder—he had only to look at himself in the glass!"

Darwin, of course, never said anything so specific. And he was careful now to say what he did mean. Here are three examples taken from the book:

> . . . man is descended from some less organized form.
> . . . man bears in his bodily structure clear traces of his descent from some lower form.
> We must learn that man is descended from a hairy, tailed quadruped, probably arboreal in its habits.

That last quotation is, of course, much the most definite. But it is very far from the popular conception of going to a zoo, looking at a modern monkey, and saying, "that is what we come from!"

The Descent of Man starts with an analysis of man's *likeness* to the rest of the animal kingdom, the mammals and vertebrates in particular. It goes on to point out that man is subject to exactly the same sort of heritable variations as are all other forms of life. Then, in anticipation of expected criticism, the book continues by discussing, at length, the mental powers of human beings, as well as their powers of imagination and of reasoning, their possession of a conscience, and a belief in a God. Admittedly, Darwin says, all these human attributes differentiate him from the rest of the animal kingdom. But they are differences in *degree* and not in *kind*. And, further than that, we can see in animals the beginnings of these higher powers, as well as how they have evolved into a full flowering in man. This is where Darwin becomes most interesting. His mind was a storehouse of examples, and he delighted in pulling out into the light a representative collection of what was stored there.

Often, he pulls out recollections of the behavior of the dogs that he had had as companions from his earliest days. Dogs, he points out, have wonderful memories; his own dog remembered him after over five years' absence (in fact, after the *Beagle* voyage) and came out for a walk with him just as if nothing had intervened. Smell, he adds, is a particularly good memorizer for animals; and, in some ways, it is very poignant with human beings, a fact we might expect when we consider how comparatively atrophied and "vestigial" is our sense of smell compared with that of other mammals, and yet how much it is a deep-buried but potent inheritance.

Even when discussing conscience, Darwin still thinks of his dogs. Human conscience, he says, is a development of a *social instinct* that all animals possess; our consciences make themselves felt when we realize that we have not obeyed such an instinct, in fact have not done our duty. "Any instinct, permanently stronger or more enduring than another, gives rise to a feeling which we express by saying that it ought to be obeyed. A pointer dog, if able to reflect on his past conduct, would say to himself, I ought (as indeed we say to him) to have pointed at that hare and not have yielded to the passing temptation of hunting it."

Then dogs, like humans, have powers of love: "In the agony of death a dog has been known to caress his master, and every one has heard of the dog suffering under vivisection, who licked the hand of the operator; this man, unless

the operation was fully justified by an increase of our knowledge, or unless he had a heart of stone, must have felt re-
morse to the last hour of his life."

Here, perhaps we may feel, Darwin is showing his hu-
manitarianism rather than his scientific understanding. But it
is all grist to his mill—the mill, that is to say, that is turning
out the material to convince the reader that men and the rest
of the animal kingdom are *not* different in kind.

Even the fantasy about the gun dog has its point. For,
although a dog does not have the power of speech, Darwin
cites examples of how nearly some animals progress toward
this power, and then points out that "this wonderful engine"
that affixes signs to objects is itself a great stimulator of the
brain. Natural selection can still be at work here: the human
progeny who fortunately chance to inherit better brains will
certainly be at an advantage.

Sometimes we may think that Darwin was too easy in his
comparison between human and animal powers and a little
too credulous in his stories of animal intelligence. There is
an amusing and revealing footnote that shows that Darwin
may have suspected that the readers of his own time might
have the same reaction. He had described the actions of a
baboon who possessed so "capacious a heart" that it adopted
and mothered kittens and puppies: "on being scratched by a
kitten it examined the little offender's feet and then proceeded to bite off its claws." Then Darwin notes at the bot-
tom of the page: "A critic, without any grounds, disputes the
possibility of this act as described by Alfred Brehm, for the
sake of discrediting my work. Therefore I tried, and found
that I could readily seize with my own teeth the sharp little
claws of a kitten nearly five weeks old." Darwin was nothing
if not thorough. As another example of this, he was not con-

tent to read merely of the report that monkeys, exhibiting the "human" emotions of dread, wonder, and curiosity, not only loathe snakes but also, nevertheless, cannot resist a fascination to look at them. Darwin was allowed to place in a monkey's cage in the zoo a stuffed snake and, subsequently, a live snake coiled up in a paper bag. Sure enough, the reactions were as described. "Monkey after monkey, with head raised high and turned on one side, could not resist taking a momentary peep."

We must not continue, however, with these human stories, lest we give an inaccurate impression of *The Descent of Man* as a chatty rather than a scientific book. There is much detailed anatomical lore in the book, much close, reasoned argument. Then there is, as we have said, the long section dealing with sexual selection and the tendency that is shown throughout the animal and human kingdom for the male to vie with his fellow males in his choice of a mate and for the female to choose or "select" the most beautiful or the strongest or the ablest. Both "sexual" and "natural" selection, Darwin shows, provide a basis on which "survival of the fittest" and the processes of evolution can get to work.

One other point that Darwin developed should be noted, because it covers an objection to his theory that is still often raised. The objection is that so comparatively little evidence has been found by way of fossils to show that there has been, in fact, an evolution from some sort of "arboreal" ape-like creature to man. Darwin's answer is the right one. First, there are many gaps in our knowledge of most evolutionary lines, for the simple reason that so many of the intervening species have become extinct. And not only that, but the chances of any particular specimen of these extinct species being, firstly, fossilized and, secondly, discovered are extremely small. The regions, he adds, where discoveries were most likely to be made, had largely not yet been searched. And here, of course, he was wholly justified. Nowadays we no longer talk of "the Missing Link." We have discovered many links—and will no doubt discover many more.

The book contains such challenging statements as that man's conscience and moral instincts, and even his idea of God, have been shaped into existence by the forces of organic evolution, and that "it is only our natural prejudices, and that arrogance which made our forefathers declare that they were descended from demi-gods which leads us to demur to such a conclusion." It ended with this famous paragraph.

> Man may be excused for feeling some pride at having risen, though not through his own exertions, to the very summit of the organic scale; and the fact of his having thus risen, instead of having been aboriginally placed there, may give him hope for a still higher destiny in the distant future. . . . We must, however, acknowledge, as it seems to me, that man with all his qualities, with sympathy which feels for the most debased, with benevolence which extends not only to other men but to the humblest living creature, with his god-like intellect which has penetrated into the movements and constitution of the solar system—with all these exalted powers—Man still bears in his bodily frame the indelible stamp of his lowly origin.

Here, indeed, was a book that was not only very human and very carefully reasoned, but also very forthright.

Yet, as has been said, Darwin's thunder had already been stolen—in fact, stolen by himself in his previous book. Or, rather, it would be more accurate to say that the public reaction to the first book—picking out as it did with an un-

erring instinct its most startling and exciting implication—
had caused the premature thunder. And the second peal of
thunder never startles as does the first. There could not be
two meetings of the British Association similar to the 1860
meeting at Oxford. Darwin got some bad reviews and some
good ones—he was unlucky with *The Times* on this occasion,
the book *not* going to Thomas Huxley—and controversy was
to some extent stirred up again. It was not stirred, however,
to anything like the extent that Darwin had anticipated; and,
however much any human being likes a fight, we cannot
imagine that he was disappointed.

The comparative lack of excitement was indeed evidence
of already achieved general acceptance. At sixty-three, Darwin was an accepted giant in the literary and scientific
worlds—which did not prevent him, however, from being
tremendously impressed when the eminent Liberal states-
man William Ewart Gladstone visited him.

12

Fame, Last Days, Influence

THE TALL, thin figure in his drooping black cloak, with the white beard and the jutting eyebrows, taking his solitary walk with only a dog for company, lost in thought, resting for a while at the gate to the path and copse that he had made and planted so many years ago—that is the final figure that we see. Darwin's last years were calm and uneventful, but still busy and, fortunately, until the very end, in considerably better health.

Botany had become his first love, and he botanized and wrote five more books, the last of which, however, returned at least partly to the animal kingdom, though in a lowly form: *The Formation of Vegetable Mould, Through the Action of Worms, with Observations on Their Habits*. This revived an interest of his father's, and it was written lightly rather than heavily; it also achieved a surprising success, Darwin being most surprised of all.

In 1877, he traveled to Cambridge to receive an honorary doctor's degree, where another set of undergraduates, equally exuberant, packed the Senate House and dangled in mid-air an effigy of a monkey and a beribboned ring, the latter to signify "the Missing Link." His last two summer holidays he spent in the Lake District, where he received the homage of an eminent American, Mark Twain, and gazed in silence and some uncertainty at the paintings by Turner that John Ruskin showed him. Pleasant and peaceful holidays they were, wherein he could congratulate himself that he was still sufficiently an ordinary human being and not a narrowed and dulled specialist, who could appreciate noble scenery even if he was not quite sure about modern art.

One disturbance he did meet. A German had written an essay on Erasmus Darwin that Charles so liked that he got the author to expand it, had it translated, added a preface, and saw to its publication in England. At the same time, there appeared a book called *Life and Habit* by that same Samuel Butler who had been a visitor to Down House and, indeed, a great admirer of Darwin's books, but who had now become a bitter critic of them. In Darwin's treatment of, and comments on, this book, Butler considered himself to have been badly slighted and, accordingly, wrote to his one-time friend some very virulent letters, accusing Darwin, among other things, of being a liar. Darwin hated this sort of thing and, although he had a perfectly good explanation, elected to ignore the letters. It was a miserable affair, but really most miserable for Samuel Butler, who could not forgive his eminent opponent and subsequently went to the enormous trouble of counting the number of times the phrase "my theory" occurred in *The Origin of Species,* as proof of its author's good opinion of himself. Darwin, however, understandably but perhaps unfortunately, continued to ignore the incident, and went on his serene and established way to the day of his death.

Darwin died on April 19, 1882, with many of his family and his wife around him, trying not to be too much trouble, calling all of them the best of dear nurses. With Lubbock, Hooker, Huxley, Wallace, and others as pallbearers, he was buried in Westminster Abbey, a national hero, forgiven for his challenge to accepted ways of thought and to the traditional God of the Old Testament.

Forgiven but not forgotten. Charles Darwin can never be

The old study at Down House, where Darwin wrote *The Origin of Species.*

forgotten; nor can his book *The Origin of Species*. It has been called the most important book of the century.

Is that an unwarranted claim? Insofar as comparisons are odious and all such statements really meaningless, it is. But it does contain a truth. Charles Darwin, by his theory, and by impressing at such pains and with such success his theory upon the world, had changed the whole way of human thinking—no less than that. No longer would the animal world be considered a separate creation of no great significance, provided by an, at times, whimsical god for man's amusement or use or occasional example; no longer could man be thought of as fallen from perfection. Now, it was seen, all life was one, and not only did the infinite variety and the strange ways of the animal kingdom have a significance of their own, but also a significance for man himself: "there but for the grace of God go I"; "that habit, that function, that instinct, is part of my legacy from the distinct past!"

Darwin's influence was, of course, much wider even than that. Not only was the whole science of biology changed; but almost every branch of human study, from embryology to paleontology, from history to religion, would from now on be considered from a new angle. A new conception had come into being, the conception of change and growth. Nothing, when one came to think of it, was static; everything evolved.

The change went even deeper than that. And here there must come in something of a discordant and less happy note. We have written as if Charles Darwin and his supporters always had right and reason on their side. We may have given the impression that their adversaries were always not only wrongheaded and foolish but ridiculous and beneath contempt. In insisting on the truth of the *fact* of evolution,

Darwin was no more than opening the eyes of the blind. But, in explaining the *means* of evolution and, more particularly, in drawing conclusions from that explanation, Darwin and, in particular, the later Darwinism are by no means above reproach.

After all, Bishop Wilberforce and his friends, however cheap and hysterical they became, did have something to grumble about. God, they complained, had been knocked by the Darwinists out of the reckoning: in their world He was no longer needed. By a set of pure chances, coupled with a bloodthirsty beastliness on the part of nature, the miracle of man, they contended, had evolved! "Ah yes," replied the Darwinists, in an outburst of materialistic optimism, "but see just how marvelous that truth is, see what promise it gives to the future! If by a purely automatic process and a grim struggle the miracle of man has evolved, then what marvelous prospects are opened for the future, what hope we can give to ourselves of continued progress!" "Not so," replied the opponents; "Evolution has produced the liver fluke and the microbe of malaria, the shark and the husband-eating spider as well as man. In any case, what is man without God?"

Undoubtedly Darwin, or, rather, his disciples (and few men have been worse served by their disciples), did add a very materialistic gloss to their findings. They seemed to glory in stressing the "animal" in man and showing that even his highest and most spiritual attributes must also be no more than the result of "natural selection."

It was against this extremism that Samuel Butler, for instance, was reacting—and he deserved better treatment and more serious attention than he received. That bad-tempered but brilliant author stressed what is called the Lamarckian interpretation of the means whereby evolution had been achieved. Lamarck's theory (of which, it will be remembered, Charles Darwin thought no more highly than he did of his grandfather Erasmus' methods) had substituted for the blind ruthlessness of natural selection and survival of the fittest the ideas of *habit* and of the use and disuse of a creature's limbs and organs. For instance, that little and ancient mammal who went up into the new environment of the trees did not lose its overdependence on smell and improve its eyesight merely because creatures so endowed would tend to survive and pass on their favorable traits; the creature succeeded because it wanted and tried to do so, because it acquired new habits and skills, and *these* were passed on to the next generation.

Now, which of these two schools of thought was right? The two schools still exist. But to prove the Lamarckian theory one has to be able to prove that "acquired characteristics" *are* handed down to the next generation—that the offspring, for instance, of a creature who has ceased to use his long whiskers will have shorter whiskers, or those of a creature that has learned how to balance on a branch will be born better at balancing. Also, the Mendelian laws of heredity, as now understood, have supported the Darwinists, to the extent of showing that changes or mutations do occur in the germ plasm, or living tissue, of the cells of the embryo and that they do occur fortuitously and in a sufficiently marked degree to give natural selection something to work upon in its winnowing process, and so to enable new species to emerge.

So therefore, we may say, Darwin is vindicated by knowledge gained since his death. He has been vindicated, too, in his insistence that man himself could not opt out and claim himself an exception to the general scheme; we no longer have to talk of a missing link in the line between man and his arboreal and more apelike ancestors, but can point to a whole line of intermediate fossil skulls—*Australopithecus, Pithecanthropus,* and the rest.

All this, of course, does not mean that there is no more to discover—of that Darwin will always continue to be vindicated—but it does mean that he was fundamentally right. Nowadays, we would at least soften Darwin's somewhat crude materialism, while still backing his main thesis. Natural selection, we would say, while being the main instrument of evolution, is not necessarily the only one. The hopeful aspect of evolution is not that it automatically produces progress—it doesn't!—but that it seems to have brought brains to the fore, to have put a premium on *mind,* so that with the advent of man it may take an entirely new course—a better course, if man will only use his brain and his mind to their proper advantage.

The trouble is that Darwinism is one of those theories that can be used to prove almost anything. Karl Marx borrowed something of its ideas of conflict and inevitable change to produce a sociological theory that would have shocked to the core the kindly traveler on the *Beagle,* the hesitant author of *The Origin of Species,* the reverent believer in a benevolent creator. At the opposite pole, the Nazis and their late nineteenth-century predecessors borrowed the idea of the "survival of the fittest" to preach the advantages and claims of a brutal master race.

There is, however, always a way of preventing ourselves from falling into that kind of error. It is, of course, to read the master with care and common sense and with not too many preconceived opinions. The man who tried so hard throughout his life to worship truth—the "dear old Philosopher" of the *Beagle*, the gentle sage of Down—would then no doubt be pleased at our self-discipline and integrity.

Chronology

1809 (February 12) Charles Darwin born.
1817 His mother dies.
1825 Goes to Edinburgh to study medicine.
1828 Goes to Cambridge.
1831 (December 27) Starts on *Beagle* voyage.
1836 (October 2) Ends *Beagle* voyage.
1837 Begins first notebook on "variations" of animals.
1839 Marries. Publishes journal of the voyage of the *Beagle*.
1842 Settles at Down House. Writes abstract of his evolution theories.
1846 Begins work on barnacles.
1848 His father dies.
1854 From September, devotes his whole time to "transmutation of species."
1856 On Lyell's advice, starts on "abstract" of his great book.
1858 Wallace publishes his paper on "varieties."
1859 (November 24) *The Origin of Species* published.
1862 His book on the fertilization of orchids published.
1868 *The Variation of Animals and Plants Under Domestication* published.
1871 *The Descent of Man* published.
1872 *The Expression of the Emotions in Man and Animals* published.

1875 *Insectivorous Plants* published.

1876 *The Effects of Cross- and Self-fertilization in the Vegetable Kingdom* published; 16,000 copies of *The Origin of Species* published in the United Kingdom.

1881 *The Foundation of Vegetable Mould Through the Action of Worms* published.

1882 (April 19) Charles Darwin dies; (April 26) buried in Westminster Abbey.

Glossary

ANTHROPOID APES: Those apes—gorilla, orangutan, gibbon, chimpanzee—that have similarities to man (Greek *anthropos*—man); as opposed to, for example, the baboon and barbary ape.

AUSTRALOPITHECUS: Literally, "Ape of the South"; fossil ape, found in eastern and southern Africa, who walked upright and is believed to have been the probable progenitor of man.

BIOLOGY: Literally, the "Science of Life"; covering the sciences of animal life and plant life—zoology and botany.

BRITISH ASSOCIATION: Full title, British Association for the Advancement of Science; founded in 1831; holds annual meetings in different cities of the United Kingdom, where papers are read and discussions held in an effort to form a better link between scientist and layman.

CHROMOSOMES: The thread-like "colored bodies" (i.e., that easily absorb a stain and so can be seen under the microscope) that are contained within the cells of all living things and on which are strung, like beads on a string, the genes; undiscovered in Darwin's day.

CORAL: The carbonate of lime skeletons of innumerable microscopic sea creatures that form into colonies.

EMBRYOLOGY: That part of the science of biology that deals with the formation and development of the embryo, i.e., of the organism before birth or in its rudimentary stages.

114

ENTOMOLOGY: The science or study of insects (Greek, *entoma*, insects).

EVOLUTION: Literally, an opening or turning out, a development; in biological connection, the proper term is "organic evolution," the development of life from simpler forms.

FUEGIAN: Native of Tierra del Fuego, the southern tip of South America.

GENES: The "beads" on the chromosome threads of a living cell that in ways not yet fully understood govern the characteristics of an embryo formed by the meeting and coalescence of the parents' gametes, or sex cells.

LIVER FLUKE: A small parasite, with a most complicated life cycle, that has adapted itself to live and breed on the liver of sheep, much to the detriment of the sheep.

MARSUPIAL: That more primitive class of mammal, in which the young are born in a more embryonic state and continue their babyhood in their mother's pouch (from Greek word for pouch or little purse).

MEGATHERIUM: Literally, from the Greek, "Big Beast"; the giant ground sloth of the Americas, perhaps the last of the early giant mammals to stay alive.

NEANDERTHAL: An early race of men, probably a different species from *Homo sapiens*, an early skull of which was found in 1856 near the village of Neanderthal in Germany.

ORDER: One of the divisions of living things as made by the biologist; the divisions run up from species as follows: species, genus, family, order, class, phylum, kingdom; humans belong to the Species *sapiens*, Genus *homo*, Order *primate*, Class *mammal*, Phylum *vertebrate*, Kingdom *animal*.

ORGANIC EVOLUTION (see "Evolution" above): An organism is any living animal or plant, anything capable of carrying on the life process.

PALEONTOLOGY: The science, literally, of "ancient things"; i.e., fossils.

PITHECANTHROPUS: Greek for "ape man"; name given to a large number of similar fossils found in Java, near Peking, and in

Africa; a creature that walked upright and had more brains than any modern ape.

QUADRUMANA: Literally, four-handed; the apes and monkeys and their like who can grip with both their hands and feet.

Q.E.D.: "Quod Erat Demonstrandum," or "Which Was To Be Proved"; always put at the end of Euclid's propositions.

TAXIDERMY: The preparing and mounting of animal skins to make them appear lifelike.

VESTIGIAL ORGANS: Rudimentary or degenerate organs that were once useful and fully developed.

Suggestions for Further Reading

Although, of course, no one should be discouraged from reading *The Origin of Species* or *The Descent of Man* in full, there is much in these books that we in these later times can take for granted; the final chapters of summary and conclusion in both books, however, are good examples of Darwin's powers of marshaling argument, and much of detailed biological interest can be gleaned by browsing through the two volumes.

Charles Darwin's description of his voyage on the *Beagle* is a book that I do not think anyone could find dull or uninteresting. Its proper title is *Journal of Researches into the Natural History and Geology of the Countries Visited During the Voyage of H.M.S. "Beagle" Round the World*. It is available in a paperbound edition as *Voyage of the Beagle* (New York: Doubleday, 1962).

In 1892, Charles's son Francis Darwin (who had acted as his secretary) published his father's *Life*, containing the autobiography and many letters to and from the great man throughout his life. The *Autobiography and Selected Letters*, edited by Francis Darwin, is available in paperback (New York: Dover, 1892).

Index